www.reternitybook.com

ISBN 978-1-61225-041-0
1-61225-041-6
Library of Congress Control Number: 2011903887

Special Thanks
I would like to extend a special thanks to several people who were very
supportive and helpful during the writing of this book:
Lynn Black Owens
Skip Wilson
Joanne Marsala Griffin
Rebecca Monroe Farmer

Editors
Denise Whittaker
Scribendi.com

Resources
King James Bible: Public Domain
NIV Bible:
Scripture taken from the HOLY BIBLE, NEW INTERNATIONAL
VERSION®. Copyright © 1973, 1978, 1984 Biblica. Used by permission of
Zondervan. All rights reserved.

Published in the United States
by Mirror Publishing
Milwaukee, WI 53214

Printed in the USA.

Reternity

Neal Wooten

Since there exists in this four dimensional structure [space-time] no longer any sections which represent "now" objectively, the concepts of happening and becoming are indeed not completely suspended, but yet complicated. It appears therefore more natural to think of physical reality as a four dimensional existence, instead of, as hitherto, the evolution of a three dimensional existence.

— Albert Einstein

***

When times are good, be happy; but when times are bad, consider this: God has made the one as well as the other. Therefore, no one can discover anything about their future.

— Ecclesiastes 7:14 (NIV)

FOR NEENAH

Foreword

June, 1963. What horrible news... I'm very hard of hearing and colorblind! At the time of receiving this news, this proud teenager felt the end of the world was nigh. My dream of joining the Army and flying helicopters was dashed (Vietnam was just heating up, so this probably saved my life). As it was, I went to work for Ma Bell, as had my whole family for generations. But because I couldn't do jobs like cable splicing, a telephone company career, which had been so good for my father, his twelve brothers, my brothers, and numerous other kin and in-laws, seemed to dead-end as a pole-climber. Even this proved difficult, as lack of communication from pole-to-pole severely compromised the safety issue for everyone involved. In less than a year, I found myself jobless, and, as the result of a bet with a friend, enrolled in a small rural state liberal arts college (the only one that I could afford).

More difficulty... no one in any part of my family had ever gone to college, hence, I had no inkling of what to study, how to set goals, etc. All of this proved that the law of serendipity can have good results. I studied a little bit of everything. In addition to the required liberal arts core of English, history, psychology, etc., I dabbled in math, chemistry, physics, geology, biology, ecology and many other fields, finally amassing enough biology hours to earn a teaching degree and eventually earning two advanced degrees in biology.

Following all of this came thirty-five years of teaching on secondary and college levels. This is where real learning occurs, and my experiences teaching chemistry, physics, general sciences, and all kinds of biology courses, coupled with hobbies of photography, astronomy, and scuba diving, helped me develop a rather multi-faceted view of how the world is put together and works.

Now the real problem: As a scientist, I see the evidences of how old the Earth is, the stages through which it has developed, how life originated and evolved (yes, evolution!) to what it (and our own species) is today. Seemingly conflicting with all this are Bible stories that, in beautiful simplicity, describe how the whole universe was created up to now in about a week! This doesn't match the evidences of fossils, radiocarbon dating, geology, astronomy, and other disciplines.

I was raised in a church environment, albeit a rather liberal Methodist one, and had heard and studied all of the dogma of the church regarding creation and development of life. At first there seemed to be a strong irreconcilable conflict between science and the Bible. This conflict still exists most anywhere you go, and what a shame! I found this conflict intolerable, as I was inevitably challenged in class by students who either really wanted the truth or who wanted to "stir something up."

What to believe? A simple, cut-and-dried magic story or a fantastically complex mystery involving billions of years, immeasurably complicated forces and forms of matter? I really don't know if it was a long on-going realization process or a sudden epiphany, but at some point it occurred to me that there was no conflict at all between the two. They were one and the same, and God is in both. Science, it seems, is merely the tool that can explain not only that God did it all, but HOW he did it! Get it...God invented Science! He invented every law of nature that determines how everything that exists must obey! From magnetism, gravity, atomic power, sub-atomic forces, chemical interactions between atoms and molecules, to forces we haven't discovered yet. And you know the more we dig, study, do research, and eventually discover, the more miraculous God's universe becomes, not less!

I really feel that the plucking of that fruit in Eden marked the moment that God chose to empower one of his creatures with the greatest gift of a gene, or set of genes, that allowed that creature to evolve (Yes, God invented evolution, too!) into having a brain with an ability to record and replay events and to analyze and store data. This new ability also carried with it a terrible, but wonderful, burden: knowledge of our own mortality. Until that moment, we and all other animals had no clue that death lay ahead (hence there was no death). As it developed, we humans are the only organisms on Earth with the knowledge that we have a creator and that we will die.

Whether or not there was an actual fruit, that act itself stands as the symbol for the moment that man received self-awareness (i.e. "realized they were naked"). From that moment on, man became responsible for his own future. His free will and choices determined not only his immediate experiences in this world, but his experiences in eternity. Here is where and when God's creation of "man" became complete. The original sin was disobedience. All other sins since then are actually derived from disobedience of some sort. From that moment on, man's life became more difficult (he was kicked out of Eden). Luckily, God laid out a roadmap to eternity complete with views of where man's choices, good or bad, would lead. Tough things happen to everybody, but we're admonished to keep the faith and follow God's rules. We're not promised a smooth flight...just a smooth landing.

God gave us this gift to unravel the mysteries of His creation and to seek out the mysteries so as to more fully appreciate the majesty and magnificence that He really is! (I apologize for the use of so many exclamation points, but this is BIG stuff!!!) I feel that it would constitute a major sin if we do not use this gift to the max, and, after each new discovery, say "Thank you, GOD!".

No one need fear science and scientific searches into the unknown. After all, what are they going to find? The truth? God's truth? Where is the fear in that?

We should no more fear truth than we should fear the path that God has laid out for us. With a simple twist of faith, my life went in a direction that I never expected, and because of that, I am eternally grateful. Given the opportunity to teach science in a rural area of Alabama has made all the difference and allowed me to aid the mental growth of the best bunch of students in the world.

It was 30 years ago that a young boy named Neal Wooten, the son a farmer, first wandered into my classroom, his eyes and mind full of a desire to learn, and with an uncanny ability to think out of the box. And in this book, Reternity, he has taken what he has learned and passed it forward. Hopefully, I had a small part in that.

Neal has done a superb job of illustrating one individual's struggle, very similar to my own, between an appreciation for science and his personal and historical faith. He shows, through Max's faith, coupled with his zealous search for truth, that we need not fear the results of our own search. After all, are we afraid of the truth?...God's truth?

Maybe, like Max, we won't always have to fearfully await death to get a glimpse of what lies afterward. Heaven? Eternity?

Thanks, Neal, for giving us an exciting glimpse into Max's search for his future, and for the encouragement that we need not fear to search for our own.

Terry J. Niblett, BS, MS, AA Cert.
Teacher, ret. — Student, forever

She peered through her large glasses as her gaze circled the room; her breathing seemed labored as her tiny frame expanded and shrank with each breath. The planning continued without her as she sat in silence, watching the dean of the university, the head of security, and the sheriff's deputy discuss how best to handle the situation with her son, Max.

She always assumed her first visit to the university would be graduation day. She led a simple life as a homemaker, a wife of a preacher, and proud mother, but this was far from it, and she felt so out of place that the weight of those feelings almost crushed her. This was not her life and she didn't want to be here. She didn't want to be anywhere — not in this time.

How could she turn back the clock? How could she go back to a better time, just one year ago when Max was still in high school, and alter the future? What could she do or say that would make her son change his course of action, the action that led to her being here today in this stifling office surrounded by those in authority in whose hands the fate of her son might rest?

How could she stop him from going to college?

***

"Are we living in the end times? Maybe we are. Throughout history, people have always believed we are living in the end times. But are these things you should concern yourself with?"

Reverend Maxwell pounded his fist on the podium. He did this often when he wanted to drive a point home. The sudden impact reverberated throughout the small church, causing those who had let the sermon lull them into a sullen trance to suddenly jump. Now everyone was alert.

The reverend tilted his head forward to peer out over his reading glasses which gave everyone a perfect view of his bald head. Only a trimmed area of white strands, which encircled the lower portion of his head like a horseshoe, gave testament to a head once full of hair. He was not a large man by any standards, but his broad, muscled shoulders and burly arms not only revealed a lifetime of manual labor, but gave the contours of his robes a formidable appearance as he stood behind the podium.

"Why are we so obsessed with predicting the second coming of Christ? Matthew, chapter 24, verse 36 says that no man or even the angels in Heaven know the day and hour of the coming of the Son of man. It only tells us to be ready; to have our house in order. That's what we should be concerned with."

Max sat in the first pew — stoic and unflinching — closely beside his mother as he watched his dad intensely. Johnny Maxwell, whom the kids at school called "Max," had been sitting in that same spot beside his mom practically since he was born. The hard oak planks were as comfortable to him as a person's favorite recliner. Now 18 years old and about to graduate high school, Max had become accustomed to his dad's tactics, and the sermons which had so mesmerized him as a child, now seemed to recycle over time, sermons with ideas with which he didn't always agree. But he played his role. In his neatly pressed jacket and perfectly straight tie, his hands cupped over each knee, only the occasional blinks of his eyes suggested life.

The sunlight of this bright spring day pierced the small stained glass windows casting distorted replicas along the walls, which resembled pastel abstracts as the five-person choir, six counting the lady playing the organ, concluded the service.

When it was over, Max shook hands as he mingled around

the small sanctuary of The Life of Christ non-denominational church in Parker, Ohio, where his dad had been pastor for the last 20 years. Congregation members filed out of the tightly enclosed pews to either talk with one another or make their way to the front entrance. After the customary greetings, Max took his place between his mom and dad as the congregation made their way out the front doors, each stopping to shake the reverend's hand and compliment his sermon.

Max towered above his mom who was only five feet even. Her tiny frame and her simple ankle-length, straight-hanging dress added to the effect. With her large glasses and her hair pulled up, which is how she always wore it for church, she had the appearance of a much older woman.

Max also trumped his dad's five-feet-seven-inch frame. At almost six feet and a measly 150 pounds, he was what the old timers referred to as "skin and bone." His slender, chiseled face was accessorized by his steel blue eyes and short black hair, which was always parted neatly on the side.

After the last person had left the building, his father looked over to him. "You better go take care of Mrs. Johnson."

"Yes, sir."

"You coming home for lunch?" his mom asked.

Without looking back as he strolled down the brick steps that led up to the entrance of the church, Max replied, "That's the plan."

Mrs. Johnson was waiting patiently at the foot of the steps; her gaze was straight ahead into nothingness as if there was an invisible object levitating in front of her that only she could see. She stood almost motionless, with only a slight sway as she held onto her cane, which made it hard to know if this was a purposeful, rhythmic movement or if she had balance problems.

"Ready to go?" Max came up beside her with his arm out for her to take.

Mrs. Johnson took his arm and smiled.

There was a cool breeze blowing. It was a beautiful day,

and the hardwood trees were a vibrant green and the wild flowers around the little church were in full bloom, giving the little two-acre lot a water-painting effect.

Max led her to his truck, an older, faded-blue Ford Ranger, opened the passenger door, and assisted her as she got inside. The truck was 11 years old and the northern Ohio winters had bombarded the frame with enough salt to rust away the bottom panels, especially above the tires, until you could see through the brown crud of the outer frame. But with over 200,000 miles, it still got him where he needed to go.

This had become a regular Sunday thing with Max ever since his dad had volunteered him for chauffeur duty. At 70 years old, Mrs. Johnson's husband had died several years earlier, and she had still been driving herself to church until a year ago when she had a stroke and no longer had the physical ability to handle an automobile. Max had been picking her up and driving her to and from church for both the morning and evening service ever since.

"You 'bout to graduate?" Mrs. Johnson asked as they rode.

"Yes, ma'am. Next Friday."

"Oh Lord, that's wonderful," she said as she patted Max on the arm. "Guess I gotta find a new ride to church."

Max smiled. "I'll be here through the summer and then I'm attending Cedarbluff University in the fall. It's not that far so I'll still be living at home. So don't worry, you're stuck with me."

This brought a smile to Mrs. Johnson's face. They talked along as usual as he drove through the small town of Parker, which began as a settlement back in the early 1800s. It consisted mostly of rural farmland, with one short stretch that could be referred to as downtown, which consisted of Hurley's Market, two convenience stores, one diner, an old opera house, and a laundry mat.

Max pulled into the parking lot of Hurley's Market, a small town grocery store that had been here since Max could remember. As he turned off the truck, Mrs. Johnson handed him her food stamp card. This was part of the trip every Sunday; Max would go in and buy her the same groceries every week.

"Be sure to get yourself something," she added.

"OK. I will."

Max went through the store collecting the small number of items. He knew this routine well and knew where each item was so it didn't take long. The fact that he worked here as a stock boy and had put most of these items on the shelves didn't hurt either.

"Hey Max. How's Mrs. Johnson?" Mary Anne, a middle-aged cashier, asked as she began to total the groceries.

"Good. She's real good." Max grabbed a small box of Tic Tacs by the register so he could show that he had gotten something for himself. He handed Mary Anne the card as she finished scanning everything and swiped it through the machine.

Beep.

Mary Anne looked at Max with a humble expression. "There's nothing on here."

"Again?" Max was surprised. "How is that possible?"

"She gives it to her grandkids," Mary Anne said. "They come in here and buy all kinds of candy and junk food and don't even leave her anything for what she needs."

"OK, how much is it?" Max pulled out his wallet. Looking inside, he realized he didn't have the $29.45 total.

Mary Anne noticed that too. "Bob!" she yelled.

The manager, Bob Mitner, a short, stocky, balding fellow in his early fifties, came to the register. Seeing Max and the groceries, he knew what was going on. He simply nodded to Mary Anne with a wry smile.

Mary Anne completed the transaction and handed the receipt to Bob.

"I appreciate it," Max offered aloud to them both.

Bob walked over to a small partitioned-off office and handed the receipt over the top. "Take this out of Max's next paycheck."

An older woman popped her head up and grabbed the receipt. "Hey, Max. How's Mrs. Johnson?"

"She's doing good." Max carried the bag of groceries and

headed toward the front door.

Once he got back inside the truck, Mrs. Johnson asked, "Did you get yourself something?"

Max held up the box of Tic Tacs and thanked her for buying them for him. He drove her home to what could be the only part of Parker that could be considered the bad part of town. There was very little crime, but the houses were older and a lot of them had been foreclosed and even condemned in the last few years. He helped her inside and then put away her groceries, making sure to check her refrigerator and cabinets for expired food.

As he drove back home through the small town of Parker, Ohio, he also wondered how the future would affect him and his life. Cedarbluff was a Christian college near the Michigan state line and only 30 miles from Parker. It was exciting to think of the new things that awaited him and a little scary at the same time. Needless to say, growing up in a town of 4,000 people and being a preacher's son meant Max so far had led a fairly sheltered life.

***

Max sat and ate a grilled ham-and-cheese sandwich with his parents. He and his dad had changed from their church clothes into jeans and t-shirts. Only his mom still wore her Sunday dress since she had begun to make lunch as soon as they arrived home. After the blessing, it was common for them to eat in silence.

"When's your thing at the college?" his mom asked breaking the stillness.

"Wednesday at noon."

"What will you be doing that day?" his dad chimed in.

Finishing the last bite of his sandwich, Max wiped the corners of his mouth with his napkin before speaking. "It's called orientation. I will be assigned a student guide, and they will show me around campus like where the cafeteria, library, bookstore, and things like that are. Hopefully, it will be a pretty girl."

His mom smiled.

His dad did not. "Are you finished eating?" he asked.

Max nodded and, at his father's request, followed him outside. They walked out to the small barn, which served more as a workshop since they had no animals. It had not been regularly maintained in many years, so you could barely make out the former red paint that covered its exterior walls. There were two doors that stayed open since the hinges were so rusted that it was feared they would just fall off if you tried to close the doors.

Max was confused about where this was going and sensed his dad was worried about something. Once inside the barn, his dad motioned for him to take a seat on a large chunk of firewood that sat upright and then stood in front of Max with his hands in his pockets.

"Uh. . . I wanted to talk to you. . . uh. . . well, about. . ."

Max couldn't help but smile at his dad. His dad, who spoke in front of people as a profession, and whom he had never seen at a loss for words, suddenly couldn't begin to arrange his thoughts.

"What's up, Dad?"

His dad looked down toward the ground as if that would help him know how to begin, as if he was not actually speaking to his son, but still practicing. "You know, college life is different. You're going to be meeting new people and experiencing new things. I read an article once that said that's the most tempting time for a young person, and that most college kids experiment with drugs and stuff."

"Dad," Max interrupted, "You worry too much. I'm not really a peer-pressure-kind-of guy."

His dad smiled. "I know that. But you're going to have new peers now and new pressures. Maybe drugs are not what I'm worried about, but maybe it's more finding a young woman and falling for her and moving too quickly — that kind of thing. I know you haven't experienced that yet, but trust me when I say it's easy to get carried away."

Trying to reassure his dad and soften the mood a little, Max offered, "Don't worry. I'll always try to do what you would do."

His dad laughed out loud, which was a rare sight in itself. "Now I'm really scared. I don't think I'm the role model you seek. Always think about what He would have you do."

Even without his dad pointing upward, Max knew exactly what he meant. As they walked back toward the house, he patted his dad on the back. "I think that was a good talk. Don't you?"

His dad smiled, glad that it was over.

Max went back in and grabbed his warehouse apron for work. As he drove to Hurley's Market, he couldn't help but wonder about what his dad had said. He had never even been on a date. He went to the senior prom because his mom encouraged him and said he might regret not ever going. He went stag and never asked the first girl to dance. He didn't know how. So the thought of him meeting a girl in college might have scared his dad, but as much as he hoped it would happen, it terrified Max.

Max finished the last bite of his pork chop and macaroni dinner, then excused himself and went up to his bedroom. Max's room was in what used to be the attic. The house originally had one bedroom, but like a lot of houses that were as old as this one, the attic had been converted a long time ago, before the Maxwells even purchased the house, to add a staircase and bedroom upstairs. The room was small with barely enough room for a dresser and bed. The dresser also served as the computer desk. There was a small closet, which was only wide enough for a single 24-inch closet door and that, along with the dresser, stored all of the clothes that Max owned, most purchased used from Goodwill stores and some even hand-me-downs from his dad.

No posters or sports memorabilia adorned the walls. The only things on the walls were three pictures, all colored with crayons, created on standard notebook paper. The lines were still visible. They had been trimmed down to fit into cheap plastic 8" x 10" frames and hung side-by-side on the wall above the headboard of Max's twin-size bed, which had at one time been part of a bunk bed. Two of the pictures were done mostly in blues and greens, but the middle one was created at the hands of someone with a little artistic talent, and you could tell it was a person with glowing red cheeks. If the average person were to critique the art, they might conclude that it was Santa Claus and two aliens. Only Max and his three Sunday School kids knew the images depicted Jesus.

As the large, dull-red sun hung almost motionless above the

horizon outside his window, Max sat and clicked the mouse of his computer, which was very old and still had the large CRT computer monitor and utilized a phone modem. With only one phone line, it meant that no one else could use the phone while he was online so he used it sparingly. It was also frustrating considering it took several seconds each time he went from one web page to another, but he had gotten used to that.

Max had gotten used to doing without a lot of things. But unlike most kids his age, he wouldn't have it any other way.

There was a quiet knock on his door whereupon his dad entered. "Hey. What are you doing?"

"Just checking out Cedarbluff's website again. Trying to familiarize myself with everything."

"Well, I don't want to bother you then," his dad responded.

"Why? What's up?" Max then noticed that his dad was holding a Bible and a notepad in one hand. "Oh, yeah. Sure. I'll be glad to be your audience."

"You sure you don't mind?"

Max shook his head. This was a common thing, and he enjoyed hearing his dad's sermons in their rough form and even being able to give critiques and, hopefully, add to them. Even though he and his dad didn't always see eye-to-eye on scripture, they did at least share a love of studying and discussing the Bible, and Max had always appreciated his dad's gentle ways when it came to spreading the gospel of Jesus.

His dad smiled and sat on the edge of the bed. "OK, this is for Wednesday night and I kind of wanted to follow up on what we touched upon Sunday morning with the end times." Coughing once to clear his throat, he began. "Today I want to continue our discussion about the end times. Everyone wants to predict when that will be. Most of us think it will be in our lifetime. But I tell you this: the end will come and it will come for everyone. It might not be at the second coming of Christ; your end could come at any time. You might think you're the healthiest person of anyone you know, but you could have a heart attack without warning. You could get struck by lightning or be involved in a car wreck. What if your end comes for you tomorrow? Are you confident in your faith? Are you ready to stand before the Lord tomorrow and be judged? Uh…"

Max sat in silence as his dad flipped the yellow page of his legal pad to follow his ideas. Before he could continue, however, there was another knock on the door, and his mom poked her head in. "Hey, Max, Carlie is here."

"Really?" He looked over at his dad.

"Go ahead," his dad nodded. "We can finish this later."

Max trotted down the stairs wondering if he had forgotten a tutoring appointment. He had been tutoring Carlie in algebra throughout the school year. His mom and dad followed behind him.

Carlie was standing just inside the front door holding her algebra book and notebook against her chest with her arms crossed in front resting beneath her neck. She wore short shorts and a sleeveless, pink, button-up blouse that accented her small athletic frame. She was a junior and a cheerleader at Max's school.

Max walked up and they gave each other a cordial hug. "I wasn't expecting you."

She smiled a little guilty smile. "I know. I'm sorry to just pop in like this. I tried calling, but the line was busy."

"What's up?" Max asked.

"I have my algebra final tomorrow, and I was hoping we could do a review," she pleaded. Her long, straight, dark blonde hair with artificial highlights came down over her hands in front of her as she stood motionless. She batted her long eyelashes over her beautiful brown eyes and put on her best pouty face, which always seemed to work with guys.

It was not necessary and it was likely that Max didn't even notice. He only noticed a person in need and that's all that mattered.

"The table is cleared off so you guys can go in the kitchen," his mom said as she overheard the conversation. She turned and went back into the kitchen to continue washing the dinner dishes.

Max and Carlie sat at the table and began to go over different algebraic problems.

"I really appreciate this," Carlie said as she patted Max on the hand. "You have been a lifesaver this year for me. I wouldn't have gotten this far without your help. I wish you would let me pay you though."

"Don't be silly." Max smiled. "I'm glad I could help."

"Do you have any finals this week?" she asked.

Max shook his head. "Nope. All done. The only thing the seniors have left is graduation ceremony Friday night."

"You're so lucky. I'll be glad when the year is over for me." Carlie rolled her eyes as if she really was dreading finals. "I wish I was good at math like you."

"I can't really take credit. With me, math is a genetic thing." Max tilted his head toward his dad who had brought his coffee cup to add to the dishes, which his mom had almost finished.

"He gets his smarts from you?" Carlie smiled at Reverend Maxwell as he passed the table.

This brought a smile to his face.

"So which one of you is better at math?"

His dad paused at the table and looked upward as if really scrutinizing the question. But it was all for show. "The one not spending a hundred grand to become a preacher," he finally answered.

Carlie laughed. "You're going to college to become a preacher?"

"Not necessarily," Max corrected. "I'm going to seminary to learn as much about theology as possible." He turned to give a smirk toward his dad. "After all, someone once told me that we are students for life and should always strive to learn as much as we can."

His dad made a funny face as if wondering where he could have heard such a thing.

"And if I do receive the calling to be a preacher," continued

Max, now looking back at Carlie, "having a degree in theology wouldn't hurt."

His dad patted him on the back for assurance and walked back into the living room.

Max's mom finished up the dishes and left them alone in the kitchen. They studied until 10 p.m. Carlie thanked him for the tenth time and left to drive home.

Max was ready to go to bed. He left a note for his dad on the fridge.

```
Got to work tomorrow from 7 to 4.  Can
help with sermon afterward.
```

***

Max got home at 4:30 p.m. after his shift at Hurley's Market. His mom was working in her small garden chopping with a hoe around her tomato plants to cut out weeds. His dad's work truck was not there.

Besides being a pastor, his dad was also a licensed plumber, and that was what supplemented the small income he made from the church.

Max walked back to the garden. "Did Dad have a job to do?"

"Yes," his mom replied, wiping the sweat from her brow. "Somebody had an emergency; I think a broken water line."

Max walked over to the barn, grabbed another hoe, came back, and started working the row next to his mom. They worked in silence for about an hour until his dad pulled into the driveway.

Walking back to the garden, his dad said, "Hey guys. Can we have a family meeting?"

"We're dirty. Can we shower first?" his mom pleaded.

"I'm dirty, too," his dad countered. "We can clean up after. I think it's time to set the college boy down and put our cards on the table."

Max's mom smiled, which made Max think to himself, *I hope this isn't another attempt at the birds-and-bees talk.*

They all walked into the kitchen and sat at the table, his mom and dad sitting across from him with a warm smile on both their faces. Max was really uncertain about what was going on.

His dad began. "First we want to tell you how proud we are of you."

Max looked on in astonishment. His dad rarely verbally expressed himself.

"And even though you're not in college yet," his dad continued, "tomorrow is your first step into a bigger world and, well, we want to send you off right."

As if on cue, his mom got up, went into their bedroom, and came back with several bags and handed them to Max. She then took her seat and looked on with the same smile that had never left her face since sitting down.

Puzzled, Max opened the bags to discover two new pairs of jeans, several new button-up shirts, and a new pair of tennis shoes. "Oh my gosh," he whispered as he pulled them out of the bag. "You guys shouldn't have." But there was no disguising the happiness on his face.

"That's so true," his dad joked. "I said you should be wearing your jacket and tie to school, but Mom here says they don't dress like that to go to college these days. I saw some of the brochures and I guess she's right. I also saw your print-off of the classes you will be taking and I figured you needed to be dressed comfortably when you take Human Sexuality."

Max felt his cheeks turning red with embarrassment. "That's a required class," he clarified.

"No, no, I understand," his dad continued to poke fun. "Whatever you learn, just make sure you come back and share it with us. If you bring slides, that would be helpful."

"Robert!" his mom snapped, now blushing as much as Max.

Max didn't even hear the joke as he had begun to lace up his new shoes. He had never owned new shoes and even if he had

ever received a pair, there would most likely have been a birthday
cake on the table. He felt like a kid again. "I really appreciate
this," he said.

"Wait! We got one more thing." His mom jumped out of
her seat again and came back with a smaller bag this time and
handed it to Max. He opened the bag to find a cell phone. "You're
going to be driving a lot so this is for emergencies."

"Mom, we can't afford this."

"No, it's a prepaid phone. There isn't a monthly service.
We've paid up 200 minutes so just keep it in the truck. There's
a car charger with it. With driving back and forth to college and
studying and still working at the store, we just feel better if you
have it." His mom was starting to tear up.

So was Max. Although cell phones were common now, he
had never owned one and had never given it much thought. But it
was the gesture that meant the most to him.

After dinner that night, Max laid out a new pair of pants,
shirt, and shoes for tomorrow's orientation. He lay awake for
many hours after going to bed as the anticipation would not let his
mind rest.

Max stepped out of his truck and stared at the campus from the visitor parking area. Cedarbluff was beautiful. The main building had been built around 1850, and the red bricks were larger than standard bricks. It was four stories high and, other than the front entrance, consisted of four perfect rows of narrow windows creating a domino appearance. Along with the main building, there were two others that had been built at the same time, and all three were almost completely covered in ivy. There were three other newer buildings as was evident by the standard-sized brick construction. The campus grounds were meticulously well-groomed and, along with the tall evergreens spread out everywhere to the green line of the woods in the background, it gave the appearance of a Robert Frost poem brought to life.

After a brief sign-in and welcome, Max found himself sitting outside the Dean of Students office, waiting with several other soon-to-be freshmen of Cedarbluff. Suddenly, a beautiful young lady walked into the room carrying a folder. Her black dress was snug in every area from her shoulders to where it ended just above her knees. As she walked, the dress seemed to slide over every contour as the light reflected off the fabric to create an almost hypnotic effect. Every eye of every guy in the room was transfixed on her, including Max's. He couldn't believe there could be that much difference in high school and college but there was proof. He couldn't help but hope that this was his guide.

"Johnny," she called out.

His heart skipped a beat.

"Johnny Thomas," she said as she peeked inside the folder for verification.

"That's me," a young guy said as he jumped up and followed her out of the room.

Max was disappointed and relieved at the same time. He could only imagine how big a dork he would make himself look in front of a girl like that.

Several minutes passed, and he began to wonder if the rest of them had been stood up. Another student entered the room, but was carrying no folder so Max assumed he wasn't a guide. He was very short, about five-feet-six, and very heavy. His shoulders and arms were as massive as the rest of him. He looked like a guy who spent as much time in the gym as he did at the dinner table. Max guessed him to be over 300 pounds. He had very curly, sandy brown hair, a double chin, and his feet pointed outward so his walk looked more like a penguin than a person. He wore a Cedarbluff sweatshirt, his matching sweat pants were pulled up over his waist, and you could see his stomach protruding below the belt line, or string line in this case. His movements reminded Max of a tank or bulldozer; not just the bulky size, but the short, quick motions they make running on tracks. But there was an undeniable rhythm to his overall appearance as well, much like the grace a sumo wrestler might display that makes observers stare in awe. The only thing more noticeable than the guy's physique was his apparent cockiness. He seemed to strut more than walk as if he was proudly displaying a champion figure.

He stopped in the middle of the room where the high school kids were seated and almost yelled, "I'm looking for a retard named Johnny Maxwell."

Max didn't move or say anything as if he was deciding if he heard correctly.

"Come on," the big guy shouted with his arms in the air on each side of him. "I ain't gonna eat ya."

"I'm Johnny," Max said as he stood up.

"Well, let's get going. We're burning daylight." The big guy turned and started toward the door without even making sure Max was following.

Max caught up to him and walked alongside. He was amazed at how fast the guy could walk with such short legs.

"So what do you go by? John? John Boy? JoJo? What?"

"I go by Max."

The big guy stopped and stared up at Max. "Good call, dude. You ever hear of Laurel & Hardy? No wait. I mean Abbott & Costello. Anyway, that's what we look like together. Maybe we should start a comedy team. What do you think?"

"Uh," Max muttered, trying to think of an answer that wouldn't commit him to anything but not offend either.

"I'm messing with you, dude," he said as he laughed at Max's gullibility. "That's lesson number one. In college, you gotta lighten up. By the way, my name's Rollo. Oddly enough, it's a shortened version of my last name also. Benjamin Rollings to be exact. I'm telling you, Rollo & Max, comedy duet. We'd be awesome."

Rollo continued to show Max around campus, and it seemed like he knew everyone there. Almost everyone they passed greeted him in a friendly way, and Rollo always took a second to introduce Max, usually as the next Romeo to woo the ladies, or other such embarrassing titles. Rollo was loud, obnoxious, cocky, arrogant, and entirely self-centered. And there was one thing Max could tell for certain about him right away — he was a genuinely likeable guy.

"Let me take you over to the most important building of all," Rollo smiled as they cut across the campus.

"Let me guess," Max offered, "the cafeteria?"

"You da man!" Rollo shouted and offered up a high-five. "I'm not just going to teach you where it's at; I'm gonna show you how it's done."

As they walked, Max took in the scenery. He loved how the neatly curved and angled sidewalks contrasted the green grass of the campus. As they neared the cafeteria, Max heard loud yells coming from an adjacent building and could see a crowd of students inside the windows.

"What's going on in there?" Max asked.

Rollo looked in the windows. "Oh man, we gotta check this out. That's Professor Nowak's class. He's the coolest teacher on campus. Every year, he gives his students an almost impossible task for extra bonus points."

Max followed Rollo as he went into the building and squeezed through bodies to get to the front. He was a little hesitant about Rollo cutting in front of people, but the big guy just pushed forward saying, "Excuse me, coming through." No one seemed to mind and several patted Rollo on the back as he pushed through.

Finally, they found themselves on the side of the campus swimming pool, which was crowded all around. Max knew that all these students couldn't be in the professor's class and assumed that most were there as spectators just like he and Rollo. The sunlight coming through the windows reflected off the water and produced dancing, illuminated spectrums all around the room. The atmosphere was so charged with positive energy that Max could feel it like an invisible force actually hitting him in the face and making his lips curl upward into a smile.

"OK, everyone, listen up," said a man holding a clipboard. He stood on the opposite side of the pool from them, and Max concluded quickly that it must've been Professor Nowak.

He was a young professor, early thirties, about five-feet-ten, with dark hair, dark eyes, and a severely receded hairline. Even though his hair was thinning, he still wore it very short, almost a shadow, which made every thin area more distinct and Max could, in fact, see his entire head clearly. He wore a mustache which actually turned down past each side of his lips, although it was trimmed neatly. If he had long hair, he might have fit right in with the 70s. He wore a shirt and tie with no jacket and was very athletic.

The professor looked at his clipboard. "Next up to take on the challenge of walking on water is Kevin Kowalski."

The student made his way to the edge of the pool alongside the professor and raised his hands in the air for moral support. The crowd obliged with vigorous applause and whooping noises. He brought out his invention, which looked like a pogo stick, but instead of foot pegs and springs, the bottom consisted of a very large inflatable half-ball. The circumference was about five feet across; the top part was flat to stand on and the sphere part was on the bottom.

"Alright," the professor acknowledged. "Kevin came prepared. Now have you tested this contraption?"

"I have, your greatness," answered Kevin. This brought laughs from the crowd.

"And have you had a successful test of 84 feet, the distance required to pass this test?"

"Close," Kevin replied.

"Then the pool is yours." Professor Nowak offered by holding his arms outward as he stepped back.

Kevin maneuvered his device to the pool's edge, positioned one foot on the thing, jumped up with the second foot and bounced off the edge into the pool. The crowd was cheering his name, and even Max was so intrigued that he found himself screaming the name "Kevin" for a person he didn't even know. The pogo ball hit the water and Kevin pulled up hard and it actually worked. The ball stayed on top of the water on the initial plunge, and Kevin was able to use his strength to make the ball go airborne again. As the ball bounced off the water, the crowd yelled louder. The second bounce off the water was harder as the ball had sunken lower this time, but Kevin still managed to get it airborne a second time, albeit a lot lower than the first. The third plunge was the killer, though, as the ball sank deep into the water, and Kevin's attempt to bounce it a third time failed so he went down with his ship, or stick, as was the case.

The crowd was still cheering. Professor Nowak had put

down his clipboard and was clapping and cheering with the crowd. As Kevin climbed out of the water with assistance from other students, he raised his hands once again as if he had succeeded. And, once again, the crowd responded.

He looked to the professor for a ruling.

"Not bad," the professor said. "Not bad at all. You came up way short, but you did it with style. I'm going to give you 25 bonus points for ingenuity."

Kevin seemed happy with that as he strutted around with his arms high in the air.

Rollo was ready to go eat now, but he noticed how engrossed Max was with the challenge so he said nothing. Max had the look of a child during his first visit to the circus. It was the look of wonderment as if no one had ever explained that such things existed in the world. They stayed for another 45 minutes as two more students tried and failed the assignment. Finally, the crowd started to disburse, and Rollo was able to steal back Max's attention and lead him to the cafeteria.

As they grabbed a tray and started loading up different foods, Rollo asked, "You got a kick out of that, didn't you?"

"Yeah," Max replied. "That was awesome."

They took their trays and sat across from one another at a table and Rollo began to eat.

"Did you have Professor Nowak?"

"Yep," said Rollo as he sipped his soda. "I had him last year."

"What was your near-impossible assignment?"

Rollo could tell that Max was definitely taken with the whole near-impossible bonus concept. "We had to propel a sheet of paper 100 yards. You could wad it up or make it into a plane or whatever, but nothing but the paper could travel."

"Did you do it?" asked Max.

"Shoot no. But I tried it because he gives people some points for trying."

"Did anyone succeed?" Max was asking so many questions

that he hadn't yet taken the first bite of his lunch.

"One guy came close. He had made it into a ball and kept soaking it in water and forming it until he had it almost a perfect sphere. Then he stuck a tee in the ground and placed the paper ball on it and then brought out a metal driver. I was thinking, *genius*. So he swings the club and gives the ball a good whack with the driver and it took off pretty well. He came the closest. If he hadn't hit a slice, he might have made it."

Max was staring off into the distance as if he could actually see the events unfold, his mouth opened with the corners curved into a slight smile.

"Another guy might have succeeded," Rollo continued as he squeezed the contents of a ketchup pack onto his food, "but the professor wouldn't let him do it."

Max looked confused. "Why not?"

Rollo explained. "It was this rich jerk so it's no big deal. He had a gunsmith or ammo guy or somebody make the sheet of paper into a bullet and he brought a high powered rifle to shoot the bullet at a target. But the professor wouldn't let him fire it and pointed out that one of the rules says that it cannot be anything dangerous. The guy complained like crazy and I think even threatened to sue the school. I told you, he's a jerk."

Max finally started to eat and Rollo added, "You probably know the guy or at least his dad. His dad is Arthur Clavin." Seeing the blank look on Max's face, he continued. "You know, the famous preacher of that mega-church in New York? What's it called? Faith for You Ministries, I think."

Max had no clue and his expression conveyed it.

Rollo couldn't believe it. "Come on, dude. He's written like a hundred books including several Bibles and has a TV and radio show. He's got like 20 million followers worldwide."

"I'm sorry. I don't know who you're talking about," was all Max could think to say.

"Forget it." Rollo returned his attention to his lunch.

Max searched his memory for some evidence of this

preacher, but couldn't find any. He felt bad that he didn't know him because it seemed to deprive Rollo of some satisfaction from telling his story. Changing the angle of the story, he asked, "What did you do for the assignment and how did it turn out?"

Rollo chuckled so suddenly that he almost lost the food from his mouth. "I looked online to see if I could come up with an airplane design. I found one that supposedly had been flown 200 feet from ground level. I followed the directions pretty accurately, I thought, but when I threw it that day, it started out flying straight then slowly began to turn." Rollo used his right hand to add the visual. He started out moving it straight ahead with his palm face down and then slowly made it bank left and tilt upward until his palm was facing Max. "It ended up landing about 20 feet behind me. Everyone was laughing so hard. The professor gave me 20 points, one point for every foot that it landed behind the line. He called them 'pity points.'"

They finished their meal, and the rest of the day went well and Max enjoyed having Rollo as his guide. Rollo walked him to his truck as Max was getting ready to drive home.

"Thanks for the tour and everything," Max said as he stood by his truck with his hand extended.

"No problem-o, Max. I was worried that I would get stuck with some lame nerd and, boy, was I right."

Max laughed.

"Seriously, dude, when you get here in the fall, look me up. I stay at Whitman's dorm."

"You live on campus? OK, cool. I will be living at home since I only live 30 miles from here."

"Awesome, dude," Rollo said with a big grin. "Now I got someplace to go on the weekends for free food."

"That'll be fine," Max smiled.

"Yeah, right. Can you imagine the look of horror in your parents' eyes when you walk in with me and ask 'where's dinner?'"

Max enjoyed Rollo's sense of humor and was amazed how

he could joke about his weight and didn't even mind when others did. He started up his truck and put it into reverse to back out of the parking spot when Rollo tapped the glass. Max rolled down the window.

"One more thing," Rollo said with a serious expression. "The first registration is two weeks away, so if you want to get into Professor Nowak's class, you better get there early because they fill up fast."

Max nodded his appreciation and drove away.

It was already getting late as Max drove home. The western horizon was a soft glow of pastel oranges and reds as the sun had gone down, but still stretched out its rays to offer the last illuminations before handing the reigns over to night. He knew he would most likely miss his parents who always got to the church early. But they would be worried if they didn't hear from him before they left. If only there was some way to get a message to them.

He suddenly shook his head and laughed out loud at his own mental block. He reached over, took the cell phone out of the glove box, and dialed his parents.

"Hello."

"Hey, Mom. It's Max."

"Where have you been? We've been worried sick. Have you been at the college all day?"

"Yeah," Max admitted. "I didn't know it would take so long. I had a great guide and there's this awesome science teacher there. He does these neat experiments." Max was still so excited about it that he couldn't wait to tell someone, anyone, forgetting that his phone had limited prepaid minutes.

"I have to finish getting ready," his mom replied, her voice so low and quiet that Max could hardly hear.

"OK, I'll tell you guys about it tonight after service. I have time to get home and clean up and swing by and get Mrs. Johnson."

"OK," his mom replied. "See you in a little while."

***

Max led Mrs. Johnson to her pew and walked up and sat beside his mom who looked over at him with a smile. He was glad he had gotten there before his dad started.

As Reverend Maxwell walked to the podium, the few whispering conversations ceased. He cleared his throat, looked down at his notes, and began. "1 John 2:15-17 tells us, 'Do not love the world or anything in the world. If anyone loves the world, love for the Father is not in them. For everything in the world — the lust of the flesh, the lust of the eyes, and the pride of life — comes not from the Father, but from the world. The world and its desires pass away, but whoever does the will of God lives forever.'"

Max looked confused. He realized he had not had a chance to help his dad work on his sermon, but this didn't sound anything like a sermon about the end times.

"And what did Paul write to the folks of the church of Ephesus?" the reverend continued. "In Ephesians 4:17-18, we read, 'So I tell you this, and insist on it in the Lord, that you must no longer live as the Gentiles do, in the futility of their thinking. They are darkened in their understanding and separated from the life of God because of the ignorance that is in them due to the hardening of their hearts.'

"Now let's talk about the meaning of these verses. What does it mean to have lust of the flesh, to have lust of eyes, pride in life, and to be separated from the life of God? The Bible teaches us that these things will always tempt us just as Jesus was tempted. Sometimes the temptations of life are too strong and can lure us away from the life of God.

"And just as some people are weaker, there are times in our lives when we are more susceptible to temptation. And as we get ready to send our young ones out into the real world, this will be their toughest hour."

Oh my gosh, thought Max as he sank down in his pew. A

feeling had come over him like he had never felt before in all the sermons his dad had preached and suddenly he felt like all the eyes behind him in the sanctuary were now focused on him. After all, he was the only one in the small congregation about to graduate high school and go to college.

Forty-five minutes seemed like hours as Max listened to his dad lecture on about peer pressure and temptation. He could sense his face was red from the dry, itching sensation now pulsating in his cheeks and the coolness of the sweat band that had formed around his neck was now soaking his collar. The room felt un-usually hot and Max began to wonder if the air conditioning was working.

When service was over, Max quickly got up and walked toward the back without even saying anything to his mom. He strolled at a steady pace, which gave no one the opportunity to stick out their hand for the customary handshake. He faked a smile and extended his hand to Mrs. Johnson, who looked surprised, and escorted her out the front door and to his truck.

After making sure she got safely into her house, Max head-ed home. He had no idea what to expect when he got t're. Was his dad angry? His dad was a firm man, but Max could not re-member the last time he saw him angry. Would he try to tell Max that he forbid him to take classes under this profesor? And what would be his reply? Max had always tried to honor and obey his parents, but he was 18 years old so what would he do if his dad tried to stop him. The truth was, Max had no idea what to expect. But he was about to find out.

He turned into the driveway and the headlights illuminated the front of the small house. Although it was a humble home with one bathroom, it had always been the most comfortable place in the world. Now it seemed foreign, uninviting, even threatening as Max sat for a minute before getting out of the truck.

Walking into the front door, he noticed that only the kitchen light was on. It lit up the side of the room going into the kitchen, so he didn't turn on any other lights, but walked slowly toward the source. As he entered the kitchen, his father was seated on one side of the table, his hands resting on his legs underneath the table, his Bible open in front of him, his eyes transfixed on the Bible. His mom was nowhere to be seen, so he assumed she had already gone to bed. Max pushed back the fear and pulled out a seat opposite his father. But as he tried to begin a dialogue, he realized he had no idea where or how to start. Finally, his dad looked up at him, a sad expression upon his face and a tear in the corner of one eye.

Max was stunned. He had only seen his dad cry one time. Max was five years old when this happened, and it was when his granddad, his dad's father, had passed away.

"I bet you didn't know that about me," his father spoke softly.

Max's face took on a furrowed brow. "Know what?"

His father tried to smile. "That I could put my foot in my mouth with the best of them."

Max let out a sigh of relief.

"I just got scared," his father continued. "When your mom started telling me about this science teacher and the impression he made, all my fears came crashing down. Sometimes I forget that fear is another character weakness that we are called upon to rise above."

"If it makes you feel any better," offered Max, "the class that he teaches, that I was so excited about, is physics and not the kind of science that has anything do to with evolution or creation. It's really more math than science."

His dad did look a little relieved. "But I saw your required classes, and I didn't see any physics there, so again, I started worrying. I let my mind think horrible thoughts. I feared my son had gone off to learn more about God, but had somehow forgotten that. I know now that this was because of my weakness, not yours. Sometimes I forget how incredible you are."

Max smiled and shook his head. "I'm not incredible, Dad; I'm blessed. I'm blessed to have two loving parents who care enough to guide me through life and to point me off in the right direction. The only thing incredible about me is you guys."

His dad finally smiled, reached over, and grabbed him by the hand, then got out his chair and pulled Max up to hug him. "Yeah," his father said as he held Max tight, "that's a much better answer than what I had."

They both laughed as his dad made his way back to his chair and sat down.

"Well, if there's no more damage I can do tonight, I'm going to bed. Your mom left you some dinner in the fridge."

His dad walked away and had almost disappeared into the hallway when Max thought of something. "Dad? Wait."

His dad turned back around.

"About that sermon tonight. . . did you come up with that between my phone call and the beginning of church? Because if you did, that's incredible."

"You think so?" his dad smiled.

"Definitely. To put together an entire sermon in an hour is unbelievable."

"Thanks," his dad replied as he turned again to go to bed.

Max opened the refrigerator and noticed a paper plate with a hamburger and potato salad on the side. On the napkin was a note in magic marker that read, *Microwave the burger*. When he closed the refrigerator door, he jumped back as he was startled to see his dad standing there.

"I thought I would tell you the truth," his dad said with a smirk on his face.

"Truth about what?"

His dad sighed. "I wrote that sermon a couple of months ago when you decided you were going to the prom."

Max couldn't help but laugh.

His dad smiled and nodded and, this time, made it to bed.

"One more," his mom said as she snapped another picture of Max in his cap and gown.

Max grinned. He found it hard not to grin and realized he must look pretty foolish. But it was one of those moments in life where the folly was justified and Max soaked in the atmosphere like a sponge.

Graduation was over as the seniors of Parker High School stood around the front lawn of the school where the ceremonies were held. Friends and family members greeted Max with hand-shakes and hugs and passed along envelopes full of well-wishes and money. Mary Anne, Mr. Mitner, and a few other employees of Hurley's Market were also there.

Most of the graduates were gearing up for celebration in the form of partying or vacations. Max's evening was a little more reserved, as he and his parents went to a nice steak restaurant for dinner. He had, after all, signed up to work a double-shift the next day at work.

"Eat up, young man," his dad said as the waiter took away Max's salad plate and replaced it with a plate with a nice juicy steak and baked potato. His dad's chest seemed to swell with pride, and his mom's face appeared to actually be glowing.

Max could sense it too. He knew his parents were proud and he enjoyed seeing them happy, but deep down he knew that it was he who was the most proud and the most thankful for having parents like these. He knew how they had sacrificed over the years to provide him with everything he needed, especially a loving environment. He felt confident in the knowledge that their faith in God had concreted his own faith, and he was ready to go out into the world and take that faith with him.

***

A week and a half later, it was time for registration at Cedarbluff, which started at 8:00 a.m. At 7:20, Max was in line, the line for students whose last names began with J—P. He was the only one in that line or any line. For 20 minutes, he was the only one in the auditorium where registration was held. Finally, others started filing in. Two students took their places at the computer terminals in front of the two lines on either side of him. Max began to get anxious hoping his person showed up in time.

Finally, at ten minutes before eight o'clock, a girl seated herself in the chair behind the computer that set directly in front of Max. She was small, short, with shoulder-length, coarse, bright red hair and a ton of freckles. Her glasses were very thick for someone so young. She hardly looked old enough to be in college. She wore an old faded t-shirt and pants that appeared to be army fatigues.

A few minutes ahead of schedule, she and the other two staff workers motioned for the first one in each line to come forward. Max quickly walked up and handed her the classes he was hoping to attend.

The girl took Max's paperwork. "Let's see here. Last name: Beaver. First name: Eager. How long have you been standing here, Slim?"

"A while," Max said sheepishly.

"Ah, trying to get into Nowak's class I see. This is your first semester here, right?'

Max nodded.

"You can't go straight into Physics 1 without a prerequisite math credit, and you can't go into Physics 2 without Physics 1."

"I don't understand," said Max.

"I'm saying, Gomer, you can't take the professor's class without at least having taken College Algebra."

"But I'm really good at math," Max pleaded.

The girl smiled. "So you're a math geek."

"Yeah, I guess so."

"Hmm," she said as she squinted and stared up and down at Max as if trying to summarize him. "I'm betting your geekness isn't confined to math."

Max laughed. "You'd probably be right."

The girl smiled as if that insult were more of a test to see if Max could laugh at himself. Her expression seemed to indicate he had passed. "I'm sure you are very good at math, but the algebra course really is required. You can take that this semester and Professor Nowak next semester."

Max agreed. He was a little disappointed that he didn't get into the professor's class, but didn't mind taking algebra.

The next two weeks went by quickly, and Max finished his first full day of classes at Cedarbluff. Over the summer, Max had worked as many hours as he could to save up money. Although he was on a partial scholarship and had a government grant, he knew there would be unexpected costs somewhere down the road, and he didn't want to burden his parents.

Two more days went by and then the weekend. Max worked and took Mrs. Johnson to church.

Monday kicked off the new week and, after Max's last class, he was leaving the main building when he heard his name being yelled somewhere in the crowd. He smiled as he knew it could only be one person.

"There you are," Rollo shouted as he came wobbling through the hallway full of students. "You thought you could hide from me all semester?"

"I tried," Max joked.

Rollo came up and gave him a bear hug, which actually lifted Max off the floor. "Good to see you, my friend. How was your summer?"

"It was good. Thanks. How was yours?"

Rollo simply threw up his hands and shrugged his shoulders as if to say it wasn't noteworthy. He then turned to see the young red-headed girl from registration approaching them. "Yo Jules, baby. You are looking so fine."

She walked up to them and stopped, ignoring Rollo and smiling at Max.

"You guys know each other?" Rollo asked.

"We met at registration. Well, kind of," Max answered, then extended his hand. "Max, a.k.a. Geek."

"Julie, Julie Blankenship," she said with a smile as she accepted the handshake.

"Jules is the most sought-after babe on campus," Rollo laughed. "When are we going out, Honey Bunny?"

Julie shook her head. "You are way out of my league."

Max laughed.

"Hey guys, do these pants make my butt look big?" Rollo turned around to give them the best angle. After a second of silence, he turned back around. "Well? What do you say, Max?"

Max replied with a simple "No."

"Are you sure they don't make my butt look big?" Rollo said, pushing the joke.

Max smiled. "No, they don't. It's everyone else's butt that makes yours look big."

Julie laughed out loud.

Rollo stood there in astonishment with his eyes and mouth opened wide. "Chalk one up for Maxie. That was excellent." He offered up a high-five, which was accepted by Max. He looked over at Julie. "Did you hear we are starting a comedy team called Rollo & Max?"

"Hey, Rollo," called out a girl from the passing student traffic.

Rollo's eyes lit up. "Whoa, gotta go, guys. Catch you on the rebound." He took off down the hall.

Max watched him disappear into the masses. "He is something else."

"That he is," agreed Julie. "I'm just not sure what. So, do you have any other classes today?"

"Nope. I was just heading home."

"Me either," she said.

They continued to walk together, and she stayed with him as he walked out through the main entrance toward his truck. It was a chilly fall day, and the sky was completely overcast, but there had been no rain. The wind was picking up, however, and it made Julie cross her arms in front of her in an effort to ward it off.

"How's algebra going?"

"Good. Really good," he replied.

Julie smiled. "Wow, you really are a geek. I am sorry you couldn't take the class you wanted. But are you going to be coming to Professor Nowak's Bible studies?"

"His what?"

"Oh, Max, you don't know about those? They're on Thursday nights at seven o'clock in the student center. I go sometimes. Rollo is always there, probably because they provide snacks."

Max laughed. "How many students come?"

"Depends," Julie answered. "Usually around 12 or so."

"Yeah, sure. I'll be there."

Max reached his truck, opened the door and threw his books inside. "Where's your car," he asked.

"Over by the dorms. I'm like Rollo. I live on campus." Several seconds of awkward silence passed. "Well. I guess I'll see you Thursday night if I don't see you on campus sooner."

"OK," Max nodded.

Julie turned to walk away, then turned back. "Hey, what's your cell phone number in case you can't make it?"

Max remembered he actually had a cell phone this time. He took it out of his glove compartment and said, "I don't know the number."

She laughed. "Well, first you need to stop keeping it in your truck. Someone will steal it for sure. Here, let me call my number and then we will know yours." She took Max's phone and dialed her own. Her phone began to play *Frosty the Snowman*. "There you go," she said, holding the screen up for Max to see. "That's your number. I'll just save it in my phonebook. Now, I'll take your phone and save my number in your phonebook. Done." She handed the phone back to Max. "Now we can call each other any time we want."

"OK," Max said with a grin.

Julie turned to walk off and Max began to think about his father's fears. "Julie, wait up."

Julie turned around and came back. Her smile seemed to indicate she was hoping he would call her back. "Yes?" she said with anticipation.

"I really would enjoy being able to call you up and talk, but the truth is, I only have the phone for emergencies, and it only has a limited amount of prepaid minutes." Max looked her in the eye for some sort of expression and seeing none, looked at the ground.

Julie's face might not have revealed her thoughts, but her thoughts were telling her that not only was this a nice, humble guy, but an honest one as well. "I like texting better anyway," she said. "What kind of a texting plan do you have?"

Max shrugged so she took his phone again and went into the menu.

"OK, says here that a text only cost you a few seconds each, and they're free on the weekend. So we can text each other. How's that sound?"

"That sounds great," Max said with a big smile.

Julie smiled back and then turned to go back toward the main building.

Max got into his truck to drive home. This had definitely been his best day at college. Reconnecting with Rollo was great, but the connection with Julie seemed more to occupy his mind as he drove home. There was something about her. It wasn't physical because if he concentrated on each individual physical aspect of Julie, i.e., the bright red hair, the white complexion, the huge freckles, the thick glasses, the underdeveloped frame, and the less than feminine attire, it didn't seem to make sense. But add them all together and he couldn't help but notice how beautiful she was.

He was still thinking about Julie as he drove right past his home. He navigated through town until he came to a large white provincial house. He parked his truck behind a fairly new Mercedes, then followed the walkway through the professional landscaping, between the columns and to the front door.

He rang the doorbell. Several seconds passed and the door opened.

"Max! Hey. So good to see you. What brings you here?" Carlie stepped out of the front door to give him a hug.

"I have a favor to ask of you," Max said.

"I owe you so you name it and, if it's within my power, it's yours," she said with a smile.

"Can you teach me how to text?"

Max got out of his truck and walked toward the main entrance of Cedarbluff. It was almost dark and the parking lot lights illuminated the area well.

He had sat down with his parents and explained where he was going tonight. They seemed to feel more comfortable about Professor Nowak once they learned that he volunteered his time to hold Bible study for the students. Max was glad.

He strolled into the student center a few minutes before seven, but suddenly slowed down. There were more than 12 people there, and he couldn't see Rollo or Julie anywhere. A sudden uneasy feeling washed over him like a wave of aversion, a sense of not belonging, like a person might have after walking in to the wrong restroom. The idea of leaving quickly invaded his thought process, and he just as quickly subscribed to that concept. He turned around and took a few steps toward the door but then stopped.

This is crazy, he thought. *I am an adult.*

He turned and walked back to where he was before and stood there. No one seemed to pay him any attention, so he huddled close to the wall. Most of them were gathered around the professor, and Max could hear the conversation and laughs, but wasn't close enough to understand it.

Someone grabbed him from behind and lifted him off the floor. There was little doubt that Rollo was in the building. He turned and greeted his large friend with a firm handshake and a smile. Rollo's hands were huge and very strong. Max wondered just how strong his friend was.

"Have you seen Jules?" Rollo asked, surveying the room.

"Not yet." Max's eyes scanned around to be certain.

"OK, everyone," the professor said. "Let's take our seats."

Rollo motioned for Max to sit beside him and he gladly accepted. The tables had been moved to the edges of the room and the chairs had been placed in a big circle. The professor was at the far wall beneath the clock. Julie came in as they were all sitting and realized there was no seat beside Max or Rollo, so she sat on the opposite side of the circle almost directly across from Max.

"Thanks," she whispered in their direction.

Before they could apologize for not saving her a seat, the professor began. "Great to see a wonderful turnout tonight. I see two faces I don't recognize, so let's meet the new folks."

Max didn't know if he was supposed to speak up, but he didn't need to. He was, after all, sitting beside Rollo.

"This here is Max, everyone. He's the new big man on campus." Rollo loved embarrassing Max who waved gingerly to the circle.

Professor looked at a young woman sitting just to Max's right and nodded to her.

"Oh," she gasped. She half stood as if not knowing the protocol, as if being half right was better than being all wrong. "My name is Jenny. Hey." She quickly sat back down.

The other students welcomed the two newbies.

"Let me tell you how we do things," the professor began, concentrating his entire attention in their direction. "At the end of each session, I randomly select three people to come up with a topic for the next study session. That's why everyone has a notepad."

Max hadn't noticed, but almost everyone had a notepad or notebook and a Bible. The NIV Bible seemed to be the most common in the room. Even the new girl to his right had a Bible with her. It hadn't even dawned on Max to bring anything and he began to feel a little foolish.

The professor, in a honest effort to educate, continued his direct line of communication with the two newcomers. "Then, over the course of a week, you have time to research and make notes on your ideas on the topics. Try to always reference scripture in your agreements or arguments. It's all pretty simple." He paused to look at his own notes. "Last week, Brad here presented us with this question: 'Is salvation from deeds or faith?' OK, Brad, the floor is yours."

Everyone focused on the guy directly to the professor's left. Brad was about Max's height, but with a lean, muscular build. He was very tan with spiked hair that began dark at the roots and gradually lightened until the tips were blonde, creating a completely yellowish surface. He was dressed in a polo shirt and pleated pants with what appeared to be very expensive shoes. He wore several gold rings.

A very beautiful girl sat to his left, although it was hard to determine that they were actually using two chairs. She was tall with very long, straight-black hair and wore a very short dress that seemed to Max to be a little too tight and revealing for Bible study. Her legs were long and tan, the left one draped over the right one and over Brad's left leg as well leaving her left high-heeled shoe dangling off the floor. She was the only one besides Max not holding a Bible or notebook, as her hands were cupped around Brad's left bicep. It seems they wanted to leave little doubt that they were there together.

"This is a slam dunk," Brad began. "Salvation is by faith alone. Paul made this perfectly clear in Ephesians 2:8-9."

Everyone with a Bible, including the new girl, began to flip through the pages.

"Got it," a girl yelled out and then proceeded to read the verse while the others focused their attention on her. "For it is by grace you have been saved, through faith — and this is not from yourselves, it is the gift of God — not by works, so that no one can boast."

"First of all, how many agree with Brad?" The professor watched as almost everyone in the room raised their hands, including the professor himself. Only Max and another guy did not raise their hands. "OK, let's start with you, Kenneth. What do you say?"

Kenneth looked at the professor, then at Brad, and finally at Max. He seemed uneasy as he finally looked down at his notes. "I didn't really have time this week to research much, but I just think it's important what you do in life as a Christian. I think deeds are a part of faith. Jesus did say to 'give to the needy?'"

"I think it's important what we do in life as well," a girl across from Kenneth said. "God wants us to do good. But I still think salvation is by faith."

Others nodded in agreement. "Does the Bible actually say 'give to the needy?'" another asked Kenneth.

"Of course it does," Kenneth offered as he defended his stance. "I'm sorry; I just don't have the verse. Anyone know where that is?" he asked seeking help.

"Matthew 6:2," Max said, his voice so quiet that some in the room didn't even hear him.

Pages began to flip. The new girl beside him shouted out first and began to read. "So when you give to the needy, do not announce it with trumpets, as the hypocrites do in the synagogues and on the streets, to be honored by others. Truly I tell you, they have received their reward in full."

Kenneth smiled as if vindicated.

"That only says when you give," Brad countered, "not that you have to give to go to Heaven."

"Proverbs 19:17," Max said, but this time in a louder voice.

"Whoever is generous to the poor lends to the Lord, and he will repay him for his deed," someone read aloud.

"Hebrew 13:26," Max continued, looking mostly at Julie or the professor.

Pages flipped and someone read, "Do not neglect to do good and to share what you have, for such sacrifices are pleasing to God."

"OK, hold it. Hold it," Brad commanded as if this was his production and people were suddenly adlibbing. "We're getting way off track. Ron, no one is arguing that we shouldn't do good works. The discussion is whether they are related to salvation. Am I right?"

Max had noticed on the registration forms that the professor's name was Ronald Nowak, but it seemed inappropriate to use it, and especially an abbreviated form of it. But the professor didn't seem to mind.

The professor nodded to Brad in agreement. "He's right. Just because the Bible speaks of doing good deeds, the question before us is — are they required for salvation?" Turning his attention then to Max, he said with a smile, "Well, Max. I see now why you didn't bring a Bible. You were the only other one not to raise your hand, so are you saying that you believe that deeds are required for salvation."

All eyes were on Max, and he almost wished he had raised his hand with everyone else and had not spoken up. But he had and now he needed to explain why. "Yes. I believe that deeds are necessary to earn salvation."

"Are you a Mormon?" Brad asked with scorn.

Max thought for a second and said, "I don't think so."

The group erupted in laughter. Rollo poked him with his elbow and winked.

The professor nodded to Max. "The floor is yours."

"Well," Max began. His throat suddenly seemed very dry. "First, there are the Commandments. Six of the ten are based on deeds, and Jesus said to enter eternal life we must keep the Commandments. Then there's. . ."

"Whoa, whoa, whoa," Brad interrupted. "I know you're new, but the rules say you have to provide scripture to back up your words. Where does Jesus say you have to keep the Commandments to enter eternal life?"

"Oh, sorry," Max apologized. "Matthew 19:17."

Someone read, "'Why do you ask me about what is good?' Jesus replied. 'There is only One who is good. If you want to enter life, keep the Commandments.'"

"And if you read the next verse, you'll see that Jesus only mentioned the ones regarding deeds." Max was starting to gain a little more confidence.

The same student continued, "'Which ones?' he inquired. Jesus replied, 'You shall not murder, you shall not commit adultery, you shall not steal, you shall not give false testimony, honor your father and mother, love your neighbor as yourself.'"

"What do you say, Brad?" the professor asked as if he was enjoying the debate.

"No dice," Brad said shaking his head. "Those are laws, not deeds."

Max didn't pay him any attention. "Then there's James 2:14-17."

The other students were beginning to enjoy this as each had their fingers ready awaiting Max's next words. This time it was Julie.

"Got it. What good is it, my brothers and sisters, if someone claims to have faith, but has no deeds? Can such faith save them? Suppose a brother or a sister is without clothes and daily food. If one of you says to them, 'Go in peace; keep warm and well-fed,' but does nothing about their physical needs, what good is it? In the same way, faith by itself, if it is not accompanied by action, is dead."

"Oh yeah, baby," Rollo chimed in. "In your face."

"Well, Brad," the professor said with a wry smile. "What say you to that?"

"First off," Brad said smugly, "no one even knows for sure who wrote that book. It was obviously someone named James, but no one even knows which James it might have been. But it's for sure that James doesn't make Paul's words null and void. Next."

Max's eyes instinctively sought out those who seem to nod in agreement. "Revelation 20:12-13."

"Got it." It was Julie again. "And I saw the dead, great and small, standing before the throne, and books were opened. Another book was opened, which is the book of life. The dead were judged according to what they had done as recorded in the books. The sea gave up the dead that were in it, and death and Hades gave up the dead that were in them, and each person was judged according to what they had done."

"Interesting." The professor grinned. "People are judged by what they have done. All very good points, Max. What do you say now, Brad?"

Brad looked upset, which made the girl on his arm look upset also. They were both staring at Max like he had stolen from them. "I'm tired of being on the defensive here. Why doesn't he explain Ephesians 2:8-9. Explain why he doesn't believe that."

"Max?" the professor offered.

"I'll try," Max said. "But I've never been able to explain it so that anyone can understand."

"What does that tell you?" remarked Brad.

Rollo chuckled. "It tells us that he's smarter than anyone else he's tried to explain it to. So don't expect any different results with this crowd."

Everyone laughed. Well, everyone but Brad and his girl-friend, that is.

"OK, when Paul mentions 'works' here," Max began as if trying to make sure to use the right words, "I don't think he's re-ferring to an individual's deeds in their lifetime. And when we talk about faith earning us salvation, we're talking about our own faith, right?"

Almost everyone nodded, not wanting to make a sound so as not to interrupt him.

"But this verse is not talking about *our* faith. It actually says, 'through faith and this is not from yourselves.'"

The ones who were not already on that page quickly flipped through their Bibles to find it.

Max continued. "This is talking about God's faith and

God's grace so, therefore, it must be talking about something else than what our faith can bring. So what I believe Paul to be saying here is that he is explaining where salvation comes from, not how to achieve it. He's saying that salvation is a gift from God, by His faith, through His grace, and no works of man could ever create something like this so we can never boast of it. No matter what we could ever construct, no matter what technology we could ever develop, we could never create something as grand as salvation. Only God can. That's what I believe Paul is referring to by 'not by works.'"

The room was silent as everyone was reading and pondering.

"And to further prove this is not explaining that works aren't important, you need only read the very next line." Max looked over to Rollo.

Rollo read, "For we are God's handiwork, created in Christ Jesus to do good works, which God prepared in advance for us to do."

Max added his summation. "The way I've always looked at it is this. Why do we not steal? Is it because it's wrong or because it's against the law? It we don't steal simply because it's against the law, is that the right reason? Or if you mow your lawn, are you cutting the grass or is the mower cutting the grass? I think you are cutting the grass and the mower is simply the tool."

There were blank looks all around the room.

"So the point is," Max continued. "We don't do good deeds simply because the Bible requires it. And we cannot do good deeds as if it's a checklist to get into Heaven. We have to make ourselves an instrument of God. That's why it says we were created to do good works. Just like the lawnmower was created to cut the grass, it cannot do it alone. Neither can we. But if we let God work through us, good deeds will be automatic. And that coincides with what James said as well."

The room was still silent. Several seconds passed.

"Well, guys. Anyone have any comment?" the professor

asked the room.

No one answered.

"I have never heard anyone explain that verse this way," he continued amidst the quiet. "I don't know if it's accurate, but I can clearly see that it is not talking about our faith, and it clearly says we are created to do good works. Very interesting. OK, show of hands, how many here think Max the Mormon is correct in that deeds are required for salvation?"

Kenneth raised his hand while displaying more confidence this time, but it was still just he and Max, still two against the entire room. Then Julie raised her hand.

Max smiled as he wondered if she truly understood what he was saying or was just being supportive.

He may not have convinced anyone, but there was little doubt in the room that he came prepared.

"If you don't mind my asking, Max," the professor asked, "how is it you know the Bible so well?"

"His dad's a preacher," Rollo said as he put his arm around Max's shoulder.

Max wondered how he knew that.

"How big is your dad's church?" asked Brad.

"Oh, it's a small church," replied Max.

"No, come on. Seriously. How many members?" Brad seemed upset and Max was wondering what this had to do with the discussion.

"About 30."

Brad laughed. It was a forced, rude, maniacal laugh. "My dad has 75,000 members in his church alone. And he has 300 branches throughout the world and has over 20 million followers."

Max remembered Rollo's story. "Oh, you're the paper bullet guy?"

Rollo looked over and nodded with a big grin on his face.

"Don't distract from the discussion," Brad directed.

"I'm sorry, but I don't understand where the discussion is going," Max admitted.

"Yeah," Julie sided with Max. "What's your point?"

Brad smirked. "He's taking these things out of context. Only a fool would do that or believe it. You guys don't see the danger here. If this is the kind of thing his dad preaches, I would warn of wolves in sheep's clothing."

"What's my dad have to do with it?" asked Max calmly.

"Because that's where you got this drivel," Brad snapped.

"Not true." Max remained calm. "My dad actually agrees with you."

"You disagree with your dad on this?" The professor seemed shocked.

"Yes. We actually disagree on several points in the Bible. We have discussions about them all the time, just not as. . . uh. . ." Max searched for a delicate word. "Not as passionate as this one."

Rollo smiled and then looked at Brad. "You ever disagree with your dad?"

"No, of course not," Brad answered. "It would be disrespectful. Besides, my dad is always right."

"OH MY GOODNESS!" Julie screamed and then started wiping at her shoes. She actually made several people in the room jump, and the two girls sitting on either side of her raised their legs as everyone searched the floor to see what had made Julie suddenly scream.

The professor's eyes were wide open. "What was it, Julie?"

Julie continued wiping at her shoes as she looked up at the professor. "You should have told us to wear waders tonight. It's getting deep in here."

Everyone laughed except, of course, Brad and company. But that was okay; Rollo made up for them.

When the professor stopped laughing, he said, "OK, I think we need to take a break here."

Max was opening boxes in the warehouse of Hurley's Market. He had a UPC gun, which, when it scanned the UPC code of any product, printed off a price tag that he stuck to the item. After he had enough boxes priced, he took a dolly and wheeled boxes out to the floor and placed the items on the corresponding shelves. It was a little past noon on Saturday. Max had been working since seven o'clock that morning and was scheduled to work until 9:00 p.m.

He could barely keep his mind on his work, however, as he kept going over the events of the Bible study from Thursday night. He had told his mom and dad that he had enjoyed it, but he wasn't sure if that was accurate. Max had participated in several Bible study programs his school throughout the years and even sponsored a few, but was always a small crowd compared to the one at the college usually only a handful of people, and it consisted mostly of people taking turns reading their favorite passages. It was nothing like the spirited debate he had witnessed, and been a part of, at Cedarbluff. That had become more of competition than a discussion, and Max was not entirely sure how he felt about it. But one thing was certain: he couldn't stop thinking about it. As surprised as he had been by Brad's attitude about faith and deeds, it got worse with the next subject.

***

"Let's all calm down," the professor ordered.

And by "all," it was clear he meant Brad, who had gotten out of his seat to challenge the girl sitting to Julie's right whose topic was "turn the other cheek."

"Sorry, Ron," Brad said as he sat back down. His girlfriend grabbed his arm again and began whispering in his ear to console him.

The professor shook his head. "Go ahead, Lisa."

The girl looked at the professor as if he had just asked her to poke a wild animal with a stick — again. In a timid voice, she said, "I just think Matthew 5:38-39 tells us not to seek revenge. Doesn't that coincide with Romans 12:19 and Romans 12:21?"

The guy sitting next to Brad's Bible study date was the first to find it. As he read, she and Brad glared at him as if simply reading the passage pointed out by Lisa was an attack upon them. "Do not take revenge, my dear friends, but leave room for God's wrath, for it is written: 'It is mine to avenge; I will repay,' says the Lord. And. . . Do not be overcome by evil, but overcome evil with good."

Before the professor could even recognize him, Brad began. "That's the problem. There are too many powder-puff Christians in the world. Matthew 5:38-39 is not saying to let people walk all over you. It's not, you know, saying that if you're getting robbed at gunpoint you should lie down and tell them to shoot you. It's not saying that if someone breaks into your home, you should let them rape your wife. It's not saying we should never defend our country and let terrorist nations bomb us." Brad shook his head, wondering how he could be surrounded by so many Biblically uneducated people with zero reading comprehension.

"Max?" the professor called out. "What do you say?"

All eyes were on Max, fingers ready on their Bibles. Max began to wonder if the professor was matching him and Brad up on purpose.

"I agree with Brad," he said.

There wasn't a closed mouth in the room as they all stared

in disbelief.

"Really?" the professor asked. "You are agreeing with Brad?"

"Yes," Max began. "Jesus is not saying anything about being robbed, raped, or being bombed by terrorist countries here."

Everyone smiled as they realized that Max saying he was agreeing with Brad was simply sarcasm to point out that Brad was entirely off base.

"So what do you think Jesus is saying here?" asked the professor.

"I think he's saying that if someone hits you on the right cheek, turn him the other also."

The professor smiled and a few others chuckled around the room. "That's what the words say," Professor Nowak replied. "But what do you think they mean?"

Max looked confused. "I think the words mean exactly what they say. Jesus was not telling a parable here. If you notice, it begins by saying we have heard 'eye for an eye' before. And we have. It's mentioned three times in the Old Testament."

Finally, everyone thought fingers at the ready

"Deuteronomy 19:21.'"

Kenneth got here first. "Then do to him as he intended to do to his brother. You must purge the evil from among you. The rest of the people will hear of this and be afraid, and never again will such an evil thing be done among you. Show no pity: life for life, eye for eye, tooth for tooth, hand for hand, foot for foot.'"

"Leviticus 24:19-20."

Someone read, "If anyone injures his neighbor, whatever he has done must be done to him: fracture for fracture, eye for eye, tooth for tooth. As he has injured the other, so he is to be injured."

"Exodus 21:22-25," Max continued.

"If people are fighting and hit a pregnant woman and she gives birth prematurely, but there is no serious injury, the offender must be fined whatever the woman's husband demands and the court allows. But if there is serious injury, you are to take life for life, eye for eye, tooth for tooth, hand for hand, foot for foot, burn for burn, wound for wound, bruise for bruise."

Max looked around the room. "So you notice that in all three places that the old law of eye for an eye is mentioned, it is about two guys fighting. That's why I think Jesus meant exactly what he said because it corresponds perfectly. I think he's saying that instead of worrying about what justice an injured party might receive in a fight, try not to let the fight happen in the first place. If someone hits you on the cheek, they're obviously trying to lure you into a fight so don't let them. Be the bigger person; be the stronger person; be the Christian."

Almost everyone in the room was nodding in unison. Professor Nowak looked over at Brad.

"I'm done," Brad said holding up both hands. "He twists everything and takes everything out of context. You should not let someone like this come to Bible study. Look at the influence he's having — just like Satan has."

The professor began to speak, but Brad cut him off.

"The thing is," Brad snapped, "you have to realize that Jesus was making no changes to the old law in Matthew 5:38-39. He wasn't making any changes to any of the old laws."

"Wait," Kenneth said. "Are you talking about all these places in Matthew 5 where he mentions murder, adultery, divorce, oaths. . .?"

As Kenneth looked down to read the verses to finish his sentence, the girl sitting to the professor's right picked up where he left off. "Eye for an eye, and love the enemy."

Kenneth nodded to the girl in thanks. But he then looked at Brad as if he could not believe what he was hearing. "You're saying Jesus was making no changes here at all?"

"Ah, come on," Rollo insisted. "The very wording reveals that he was making some kind of changes. Every one of those verses begins with 'you've heard this, but I tell you this.'"

Brad persisted. "You guys can't even understand what you read. Jesus was clearly making no changes here but only affirming that the old laws were still valid."

"Max?" the professor jumped in. "What do you say?"

Max looked at Rollo and Kenneth. "I agree with these guys; it's obvious that Jesus was making some changes. The way I've always thought of it is this: throughout the New Testament, Jesus is raising the standard for being a Christian. He's making it tougher, not easier. The old law was not to commit adultery, the new law is don't even think about it. It was don't murder and now it's don't even be angry. It was love your neighbor and hate your enemy, but now it's love also your enemy. And, of course, eye for an eye is now turn the other cheek. This coincides with the entire message of the New Testament. Everything Jesus taught raised the standards like loving instead of hating, forgiving instead of retaliation, peace instead of war. He raised the standard, and it's our responsibility to honor that and raise our standards as well."

Everyone was silent, especially Brad who seemed to not even be paying attention.

"Brad?" the professor called out.

Brad held up his right hand without looking at the professor or anyone else.

"So you have no rebuttal?" the professor asked again.

Brad turned in his chair to face his girlfriend. "I don't cast my pearls before swine."

Max looked over at Rollo who was enjoying himself in misery. He was chuckling so hard that his belly was shaking all over. Max looked at Julie who had a huge smile and seemed to be beaming with pride. Max had never experienced these kinds of feelings before.

***

"Hey." The manager of the store, Mr. Mitner, patted Max on the back, which made him jump. "Whoa. Sorry. Didn't mean to startle you."

"Sorry," said Max. "My mind was in another world."

Mr. Mitner laughed. "Well I hate to be the one to bring you back to this one. How's college going anyway?"

"Really good. Thanks."

"I remember my first year in college," Mr. Mitner said. "I was pretty excited and scared, too. I remember wondering how could there be so many beautiful women all in one place."

Max smiled. He knew the feeling. He was also surprised since this marked the only personal conversation he had ever had with Mr. Mitner.

"Speaking of which," Mr. Mitner continued, "there's a young lady out front asking for you."

Max looked confused. He walked over to the middle of the back-room area so that he could look through the small windows in the double doors that swung both ways to enter and exit the warehouse. It was Julie. Max smiled. "Yeah, she's a classmate from Cedarbluff."

"Well I guess you better take your lunch now, then Mr. Maxwell," the manager said. "In fact," he added, "since you're working a double-shift, you should take two hours for lunch." This was followed by a quick wink as the store manager turned to walk away.

Max clocked out and walked through the warehouse doors. Julie spotted him and stood motionless, letting him walk up to her.

"Hey, Julie. What are you doing here?"

"Just wanted to see where you worked. You told me you were working all day so I thought I would come by and check it out. Do you get a break anytime soon?"

Good old Mr. Mitner, thought Max. "I just clocked out for a two-hour lunch."

"Great," Julie smiled. "You can show me around town and take me to the best place to eat."

"OK," said Max, his eyes looking at an angle upward as if trying to determine where that place was. "I'll be right back," he said as he turned to go back toward the warehouse.

"Where are you going?"

Max turned back with a big smile. "I have to make a reservation."

Max navigated and donned the tour guide hat as Julie chauffeured him through the small town of Parker, the most interesting area being downtown, which still consisted of the buildings first built over a hundred years ago. Max pointed out the old opera house, which was still used for school plays and other special occasions.

As they rode around, Julie slowly changed the subject from the town. "What did you think of Bible study?"

"To be honest, I'm not sure I enjoyed it at all." Max searched her face for expression as he spoke. "I don't really care for confrontation and I didn't mean to upset that guy."

"You can't not upset Brad," Julie reassured. "He's like that every session. Most people just say nothing to avoid him, or it turns into a heated argument that the professor has to quell. That's why I enjoyed your points. He was angry because you made sense, and he couldn't think of what to say to combat your points. The fact that you remained calm made it worse."

Julie was smiling but Max was not. "But that's the point," Max said honestly. "Bible study should not be about combat. It's okay to differ, but trying to hold or prove the other wrong is not for God's glory but for your own."

Julie nodded. She knew Max was right, but decided to lighten the mood. "I advise that I can't talk with you about this. I'm not going to cast my pearls before swine."

They both laughed.

"So where are we eating?" she asked. "Are they ready for us because I'm starving?"

Max directed Julie back through town and into a rural setting. He pointed to a driveway and had her pull in and park behind a plumber's truck. Julie was confused. It didn't look like a restaurant. She looked at Max for confirmation but he simply smiled and motioned for her to get out. They walked to the door and Max went inside with Julie in tow.

"There you guys are," Max's mom shouted from the kitchen. "We're ready so get washed up."

The smell of home cooking permeated the small house. Max walked into the kitchen and introduced Julie to his parents. It was hard to tell who was smiling more, Max, his parents, or Julie.

After they went to the bathroom to wash their hands, they seated themselves at the table across from his parents. "Just dig in," his mom said as she spread out her hands with her palms open as to show them where the food was.

In front of them was a very nice spread considering the short notice. The main platter had grilled-cheese sandwiches and BLTs, all of which had been sliced from one corner to the other leaving triangle-shaped halves. Then, there was salad, chips, and a plate of vegetables consisting of baby carrots, cucumbers, and little tomatoes.

"I was just going to make BLTs," his mom said, "but I didn't know if you were a vegetarian. I read that a lot of college girls are."

Julie smiled. "Oh no. Don't try to take my bacon away from me."

The reverend looked at Max with a big smile. It was obvious that he liked Julie. "Son, would you like to ask the blessing?"

Max obliged.

After the blessing, they all began to fill up their plates. "So," Julie said, looking at Max's parents, "how often does he bring a new girl home for this royal treatment?"

His dad laughed. "Are you serious? We didn't even know Max knew what a girl was."

Everyone laughed.

"So don't think this is common," his dad continued. "In fact, I can tell you how not common this is. I didn't even know we still owned porcelain plates."

Everyone enjoyed lunch and afterward Julie drove Max back to the store. "I'll see you at school next week," she said as Max got out. "And I'll see you Thursday night at Bible study?

Right?"

Max gritted his teeth. "I don't think so."

"You have to come," she pressed. "You named one of the topics, remember?"

"Yeah," Max muttered, "but still. I just don't know if I can go through that again. I think it's messing with my head. I had a dream last night about it."

Julie laughed. "What was the dream about?"

Max grinned and waved his hand as if to say it was too strange to talk about, but Julie persisted. "It was dumb," Max began. "I dreamed that Jesus came to the Bible study and wasn't happy."

"That's a sign," Julie said, acting serious. "Don't you think that's a sign?"

"I don't know."

"You do believe in signs, don't you?" Julie asked.

"Sure," Max offered weakly.

Julie tried another angle. "You do realize you get to see me there, don't you?" She waited for Max to smile. "Well, there's the best reason I can think of."

Max relented. "OK, I'll be there."

Walking into the student center brought about a different reaction from Max's first visit. No one ignored him this time. Most patted him on the back and at least two, including Rollo, bowed to him. Max found it hard not to grin and blush.

It seemed like exactly the same crowd and everyone took their seats. Julie ended up across from Max again as neither Rollo, nor the new girl, named Jenny, seemed willing to relinquish their seats on either side of Max.

Max had decided to limit his responses, which turned out to be fairly easy this time. At the end of the last session, the professor had called upon Rollo to come up with the first topic of discussion. As Rollo contemplated, Brad offered his help.

"How about gluttony?" Brad smirked.

Rollo slapped his knee and let out an exaggerated laugh. Then he fired back. "My topic is — 'Can Rich People Go To Heaven?'"

When the professor called upon him this night, Rollo named off a bunch of verses as the others tried to be the fastest to find and read them. Among them were verses from Matthew 19 about the rich man asking Jesus what he must do to get eternal life. The most notable line, of course, comes when Jesus says that it is easier for a camel to go through the eye of a needle than it is for a rich man to enter the kingdom of Heaven.

Brad Clavin, who automatically thinks he should be the first to respond, fired back with a cache of verses that seemed to make little sense to Max. In fact, they seemed to make little sense to anyone.

Others threw in their own views, but when the professor called upon Max, he simply said, "I don't have anything to add. Rollo summed it up well."

The second topic was about how old the universe was and arguments ranged from 6000 to six billion years. When the question was presented to Max, he replied, "I don't have an opinion on this."

"You must have some thoughts," the professor pushed. "None of us know the answers for sure so your thoughts don't have to be right."

Max wished he could have stopped the next statement before he made it. "I don't think we're supposed to argue these things."

"What a hypocrite," Brad blurted out. "Last week, this guy wouldn't shut up and stop arguing, and now he says we shouldn't. You're guilty of the very thing you're accusing us of."

Max shook his head. "Last week we were discussing scripture, which the Bible instructs us to do. This topic is not in the Bible. This topic is a science question and, as Professor Nowak pointed out, none of us know the answer. On these topics, I believe the Bible says to not argue."

Everyone was looking at him as if he had forgotten something.

"Oh," Max said as he realized. "Proverbs 3:5"

Someone read. "Trust in the Lord with all your heart and lean not on your own understanding."

"Timothy 6:20," added Max.

"Timothy, guard what has been entrusted to your care. Turn away from godless chatter and the opposing ideas of what is falsely called knowledge."

People started nodding again, which drove Brad crazy.

"Wait. . . wait," he yelled. He began flipping vigorously through his Bible. He then handed it to his girlfriend, went into his backpack, brought out an electronic Bible, and started typing in search words.

"Why don't you just ask Max?" Rollo said laughing.

"I can't find it, but the Bible says you should always be prepared to give an answer," Brad said without looking up from his device.

"1 Peter 3:15," Max said.

Fingers began to flip and Jenny yelled out. "Got it." Then she read, "But in your hearts, revere Christ as Lord. Always be prepared to give an answer to everyone who asks you to give the reason for the hope that you have. But do this with gentleness and respect."

Brad put down his electronic Bible to reveal a smug look of satisfaction. He stared at Max and asked, "What does that say to you?"

Max tried to give an honest answer that would not sound like he was making fun of Brad. He did not succeed. "It says to me that we should always be prepared to give an answer for the hope that we have. It even tells us to do this with gentleness and respect, some of those powder-puff traits."

"So, Brad, let me ask you," Rollo said, taking Max's lead, "if someone comes up and, you know, asked you about the hope you have in you, are you going to answer by saying how old you think the universe is?"

"If that's what they're asking about, yes."

Rollo shook his head.

This debate went on without Max, and he was feeling better being out of the circle and out of the spotlight. But he could not avoid getting into the fray with the third topic since he had picked the subject for that one.

After the second topic was talked out, Professor Nowak looked at his notes. "OK, Max. The third topic you picked out was 'Should Christians Call Others Names?'"

Quiet snickers filled the room.

"Why did you pick that topic?" asked the professor.

Max shrugged his shoulders. "I've just never been to a Bible study where Christians call other Christians names. Actually, I've never been anywhere where Christians call other Christians names. In two visits, I've been called Mormon, fool, powder-puff, swine, and hypocrite. So I was wondering if it was a common thing."

"And your scriptural support?" the professor asked.

"I think the uniform message in the New Testament goes against that, but more specifically, there's Matthew 5:22."

Julie already had her page marked there so she was the first. "But I tell you that anyone who is angry with a brother or sister will be subject to judgment. Again, anyone who says to a brother or sister, 'Raca,' is answerable to the court. And anyone who says, 'You fool!' will be in danger of the fire of hell."

Everyone turned toward Brad, but he sat motionless with a confident look upon his face.

"Anyone?" the professor threw out to the room.

When no one answered, Brad asked, "May I?"

The professor nodded and Brad began. He had obviously come prepared. "Matthew 23:15."

Someone read, "Woe to you, teachers of the law and Pharisees, you hypocrites! You travel over land and sea to win a single convert, and when you have succeeded, you make them twice as much a child of hell as you are."

Brad continued, "Matthew 23:16."

"Woe to you, blind guides! You say, 'If anyone swears by the temple, it means nothing; but anyone who swears by the gold of the temple is bound by that oath.'"

"Matthew 23:17," he added.

"You blind fools! Which is greater: the gold, or the temple that makes the gold sacred?"

"Matthew 23:27."

"Woe to you, teachers of the law and Pharisees, you hypocrites! You are like whitewashed tombs, which look beautiful on the outside but on the inside are full of the bones of the dead and everything unclean."

"Matthew 23:33."

"You snakes! You brood of vipers! How will you escape being condemned to hell?"

Brad sat back with a smug expression. His girlfriend's eyes gleamed in defiant pride.

The professor looked at Max. All other eyes followed.

Max looked back at everyone for a second. He didn't know exactly what to say. "Uh. . . I don't know what that means. The discussion was whether Christians should call people names, not whether or not Jesus used words to identify people, especially the scribes and Pharisees."

"Just admit it. You got wiped on this one." This was the happiest anyone had seen Brad since Max joined the group a week ago.

"But I still don't see the connection," Max admitted.

Brad shook his head. "OK, farm boy, let me ask you this. Who was the only person without sin?"

"Jesus," Max conceded.

Brad smiled a devious smile as if he had just gotten a big game animal to step into a snare. "So if Jesus never sinned and he called people names, then calling people names must not be a sin." Brad sat back and gloated; the only thing he forgot to say was "the defense rests."

Max smiled and nodded. *That was his angle*, he thought to himself. All eyes were on him, so he offered his rebuttal. "First, I do not refer to what Jesus did as calling names. Jesus could see into people's hearts and identify them for who and what they were, so it wasn't a matter of immature name calling. That's not a gift that God chose to bless us with. Secondly, we are not Jesus, and the Bible never tells us to emulate him; only to obey him."

Kenneth chimed in with a smile. "What about the bumper sticker that says, 'What Would Jesus Do?'"

Max smiled back. "Are you seriously asking me to consider which I trust more: a bumper sticker or the Bible?"

Several people giggled and Kenneth gave Max a nod.

"I think the bumper sticker should read, 'What Would Jesus *Have* Us Do?'" Max added.

"Wait," Brad jumped in, afraid that his snare was deteriorating. "The Bible tells us to try to be like Jesus."

Max tilted his head, raised his eyebrows, and turned his hands over to reveal his palms. Everyone knew what he meant — where's the verse to back this up?

Frustrated, Brad grabbed his electronic Bible again and started punching buttons. His teeth clinched and his forehead became more and more red as he couldn't find what he was looking for.

Max did not wait for him. "See, I think this sheds light on a very murky problem. We are not God. We are nowhere near on the same level as He. So we cannot use the Lord's actions to ignore His teachings. And if you think about it, this was Satan's first trick. Genesis 3:4-5."

That caught them off-guard as they grabbed their Bibles and started flipping once again. It wasn't far to flip. Rollo won the race.

"'You will not certainly die,' the serpent said to the woman. 'For God knows that when you eat from it, your eyes will be opened, and you will be like God, knowing good and evil.'"

Everyone except Brad and his girlfriend sat in amazement, most of them nodding with smiles on their face.

"Wow," said Kenneh. "I never thought of it that way. I've always said, 'What would Jesus do' myself. But you're right; that was Satan's first trick."

"And still his best trick, it seems," added Julie.

The professor got in the last words with, "If it ain't broke, don't fix it." The session had long expired so the professor called it a night.

Max, Rollo, Julie, and Jenny walked out of the class and out of the building together. Jenny seemed to fit right into the group or, at least, wanted to fit in. Everyone included her in conversation to make sure she felt a part.

"See you mañana, champ," Rollo said as he turned to go to the dorms.

Max stood there at his truck with Jenny and Julie. A moment of awkward silence passed, as Julie seemed to be wondering when Jenny was going to excuse herself. But she never made a motion to do that.

"Well, that was another good session," Julie said, breaking the silence.

Jenny agreed. "You make the class very interesting."

Julie was wanting to tell her that she had never attended a session without Max, so how would she know how exciting or unexciting Bible study was before Max started attending. Instead she said, "Well it's late and you got a long drive so we better let you go."

Jenny took her cue. "Yes, drive carefully, Max."

The two girls walked back to the dorm buildings together as Max got into his truck and drove home.

"OK, I'm putting a stop to this," the professor said, raising his hands. "Brad, sit back down."

Max couldn't believe he found himself in the same place for a third straight Thursday and wondered again why he came. The tension in the air was so thick that everyone in the circle felt caught up inside it as if it was a tangible substance that had replaced the very air in the room. To Max, it was almost stifling, and he could hear his own heartbeat as he sat uncomfortably in his chair.

"We've gotten way off the discussion," the professor continued. "The discussion isn't about the Elect, or chosen ones, or saints, or whatever you want to call them. The discussion wasn't about if those make up everyone saved or only a small percentage; the discussion was about judging. What was the topic again Julie?"

"Should Christians Judge?" replied Julie.

"OK, Brad says it's a Christian's place to judge and used 1 Corinthians 6:2 of the King James Bible, which is Paul saying that the saints will judge the world. Now Max, you began by arguing that 'the saints' here meant the chosen ones, and that's where the debate went off the rail. You believe the saints make up a small portion of those saved, and Brad thinks they make up everyone saved. We all get that. I think the Elect would make a great topic, but right now we're talking about judging others so let me see if I can get us back on track. Brad, explain again why you feel judging is something Christians are supposed to do."

"It's simple," Brad replied. "The Bible says we are supposed to discern right from wrong. How else are we to know what we are supposed to do or teach others to do? That's judging."

"Wait," Kenneth said, entering the discussion. "Is that judging?"

"That's discerning," Rollo chimed in.

The professor raised his hands again. "Then that's what we need to do first. We need to decide what we're talking about when we say 'judging.' Julie, this is your discussion so you clarify."

Julie thought for a second and then smiled at Max. "Max, I'll let you explain. What do you think Jesus is talking about in the Sermon on the Mount when he says to judge not?"

"That's not fair," Brad complained.

Julie smiled. "It's my topic and I can let anyone I want to help with it."

The professor agreed. "Max, what do you say?"

Max thought it was simple, but thought for a second how best to convey it. "Jesus is not talking about deciding right from wrong. Of course, we are all supposed to do that. If you decide that killing is wrong, that's not judging someone. Discerning any action as right from wrong is not what this is about. But if someone kills and you decide that person is condemned for it, or that that person doesn't deserve to be saved, that's what we're talking about here."

There were nods once again all around the room.

Max continued. "But I think it goes deeper than that, too. I think something that we're all guilty of doing is thinking another person's sins are worse than our own and that is judging also."

The professor said, "Give us an example of that."

"OK," Max replied. "Two sins mentioned in the Bible are homosexuality and lying. I believe that almost everyone, if not everyone, is guilty of lying, whereas a very small percentage of the population is guilty of the other. Lying is also mentioned hundreds of more times in the Bible than homosexuality and is even one of the Commandments. Yet, there seems to be many more sermons on homosexuality than on lying. So I think we tend to think one is worse than the other."

"It is!" shouted Brad.

Max and several others around the room shook their heads in frustration at the mentality of Brad, although each knew it was pretty common amongst Christians to single out this particular sin to preach against. Maybe some of them had friends who were gay and that, as much as anything else, allowed them to have deeper, and more forgiving, feelings. Max didn't even know anyone who was gay. He was certain that there were gay people at his high school because he had overheard remarks from other students, but he was too naïve to even know who they were referring to.

The head shakes began to annoy Brad. "Homosexuals cannot be Christians."

This made almost everyone start to mutter.

The professor raised his hands to quiet the room. "Why do you say that, Brad?"

"They just can't."

"That's a lame answer," Julie snapped.

"They're sinners," Brad fired back. "No homosexual will ever go to Heaven."

This brought several people to their feet in protest.

"Whoa," interceded the professor again. "Let's save this for another topic. OK? We're getting way off topic. Max, continue with your points on judging."

"That's about it. That's what I think Jesus is referring to during the Sermon on the Mount."

The professor looked around the room. "Is everyone satisfied with that?"

Everyone nodded, even Brad.

"OK," said the professor. "Now that we know what we're dealing with, Brad, what do you say about Matthew 7:1, which was Julie's first point? During the Sermon on the Mount, Jesus clearly said 'judge not.'"

Brad stood back up. "OK, you have to take this in the context of the time. Jesus is talking to the scribes and Pharisees here. Back then, that's how these guys operated. They sat in judgment of everyone. They were very condemning and judgmental, so that's why Jesus is telling them they're not the ones to judge because their judgments were wrong. See, Jesus is not telling Christians not to judge, but rather that Christians are supposed to be the judges."

The professor turned to Max. "What do you say to that?"

Max tried to think about where to start. "First of all, I don't think Jesus was talking to the scribes and Pharisees here. The Sermon on the Mount begins by saying that His disciples came to Him and He began to teach them. At the end, it says that others had gathered around, which I believe would mean His followers."

"The scribes and Pharisees were always around trying to catch Jesus saying something wrong," interrupted Brad.

Max shook his head. "I think that's true for when Jesus spoke in the cities and towns, but I don't see the scribes and Pharisees out roughing it in the wilderness with His followers. But even if there were some in the crowd, the Bible says He was teaching His disciples. And on the Faith for You website, your dad even says that all elements of the Sermon on the Mount apply to us today and, if you want to make sure you're living life right as a Christian, hold yourself up to the Sermon on the Mount."

Brad's eyes were glaring. How dare anyone use his father's words against him. "This is Bible study, not internet study. You're supposed to use scripture to defend your position."

"He's right," said the professor.

"OK," said Max. "Romans 14:10."

Someone read, "You, then, why do you judge your brother or sister? Or why do you treat them with contempt? For we will all stand before God's judgment seat."

"1 Corinthians 4:5."

"Therefore, judge nothing before the appointed time; wait until the Lord comes. He will bring to light what is hidden in darkness and will expose the motives of the heart. At that time, each will receive their praise from God."

"James 2:4."

"Have you not discriminated among yourselves and become judges with evil thoughts?"

"James 4:11."

"Brothers and sisters, do not slander one another. Anyone who speaks against a brother or sister or judges them speaks against the law and judges it. When you judge the law, you are not keeping it, but sitting in judgment on it."

Max continued. "So I don't think Jesus was telling the scribes and Pharisees not to judge because their judgments were condemning or judgmental, because all judgment is judgmental and all judgments have the possibility of being wrong, no matter who makes them. Such is the nature of judging."

"John 7:24 of the King James Bible," Brad said, with his arms crossed in defiance.

Only two people had brought a Kings James Bible, so they searched and one of them read. "Judge not according to the appearance, but judge righteous judgment."

"Get the picture?" smirked Brad. "That's Jesus telling us not to judge by appearances but judge righteous judgment. That's the same thing I've been saying."

All eyes turned to Max.

"Jesus was not talking to us," Max began. "or to his disciples or followers. He was talking to the Jewish leaders of that time who were complaining that he had broken the law of Moses for healing a man on the Sabbath. He was showing them how silly it was for them to judge at all. Let me ask a question. Were the Jewish people back then qualified to judge Jesus?"

The room was silent.

"The question was for everyone," Max clarified.

Everyone either shook their head or said, "No."

"That's right. None of us are qualified to judge Jesus. But for this to mean what Brad is claiming it means, then Jesus would have to be stating that these people are qualified to judge Him."

"There he goes again," said Brad, "twisting everything and taking it out of context."

Addressing Brad's first choice of scripture, Max added, "And even if Brad is right that we do not have free will to accept Jesus and the saints do make up everyone who will be saved, 1 Corinthians 6:2 still does not instruct Christians to judge others. It's talking about the future. It says the saints *will* judge the world and if you *are to* judge the world and that correlates perfectly to what Revelation says about judgment day."

Brad threw up his hands.

Ignoring Brad, Max gave his summation. "So yes, decide right from wrong. Teach right from wrong. If someone is doing wrong, try to help them see the error of their ways. But do not try to judge a person's heart because we're not qualified. Do not judge whether a person has the right to be saved because that belongs to God. Do you turn away from those who could be saved because you feel their sins are worse than your sins? Just follow the simple-to-understand instructions that Jesus was delivering to all Christians, past, present, and future, and judge not."

The room was so quiet you could have heard a pin drop. Brad sat with his head down, shaking it from side to side. His girlfriend sat and tried to comfort him. The rest of the group sat in awe. Rollo sat and nodded while occasionally pointing his thumb in Max's direction while looking out at everyone else as if to convey that Max was his prodigy.

Julie sat with a look of genuine appreciation. "I rest my case," she said with a smile.

❧10❧

Sunday afternoon, after the morning service, Max sat in his room researching the website for the Faith for You Ministries. Before going to the Bible study and hearing the views of Brad Clavin, he never knew that there were people out there with these beliefs. And he certainly never knew they would have such a large following. One thing became clear as he read through the many sermons of Arthur Clavin – all of Brad's ideas were from his father, most of them recited verbatim.

Max's dad walked up the stairs and stood by his open bedroom door then knocked on the doorframe. Max looked up and motioned for him to come in, which he did and took a seat at the end of the bed.

"Doing homework?"

"No," Max answered. "I'm reading over this fellow I read about, his preacher and his ministries, and I can't believe that I'm reading."

The reverend was curious. "Who is it?"

"His name is Arthur Clavin. He's from New York, and his church is a non-denominational church called Faith for You."

"Oh, Dr. Clavin, huh?" his dad replied.

"You know him?" asked Max.

"I know his organization. Ever so often, someone contacts us from their church to pitch the idea of us becoming a Faith for You branch. They claim it will make us more profitable even after giving them their cut."

Max asked, "Have you studied any of his teachings?"

His dad shook his head. "No, but whenever I go to the conferences, I hear a lot of preachers talking about his teachings, some even saying his teachings are borderline heresy. Why are you so interested all of a sudden?"

Max told his dad everything. He told him about Brad and the things he argued about in Bible study. He told him about the aggressive and rude way he argued his points. He read off parts of sermons from the internet that coincided with Brad's views. He told him about how Bible study, in only two sessions, had evolved into almost a competition between him and Brad. He told him how some of the other students treated him like a big shot in class and how it made him feel uncomfortable.

When Max finished, his dad, who had been listening intensely, asked a simple question. "Do you enjoy going?"

Max had to think on that one. "I think that's the problem; I enjoy it too much."

His dad smiled and asked, "Meaning?"

Max knew his dad understood where he was going with this, but was not going to help at all.

"Meaning I might need that peer pressure sermon again," Max laughed. "I feel like I'm getting off the path when I'm in there. It's a great feeling to have people stroking your ego. It's a feeling I've never had before. But I try to keep reminding myself why I'm going to college in the first place. It is not for my glory, but for His. It is not for worldly gains, like being the champion Bible debater or anything like that."

His dad nodded, then surprised Max by getting up and heading out the door without commenting on what Max was talking about. Instead, as he walked toward the door, he said, "OK, well, I'll see you when you come down."

He had gotten all the way out of the door and out of sight before Max was able to focus. "Dad! Wait!"

"Yes?" he asked innocently as he poked his head back inside.

Max was puzzled. "Well, aren't you going to say anything?"

"About what?" his dad continued the fallacy.

"About what I just said?"

"I don't have anything to say," his dad replied. "I don't have any ideas or words that could make it any clearer than you just did. Sounds to me like you know what to do, but just needed someone to say it out loud to, in which case my job is done and I think I did it very well." He smiled and walked downstairs.

***

Max sat across from Julie in the cafeteria. They had discovered that they each had the 10:00 a.m. slot free on Mondays and had decided to meet in the cafeteria. Max was deciding how to broach the subject with Julie and only hoped it would go as smoothly as it did with his dad.

"I think this was a good idea — meeting here every Monday morning," Max began.

Julie smiled and nodded to signify her concurrence.

"I was thinking also that you could come to our house for dinner more often," he continued.

Julie's smile got bigger.

"And thought maybe we could hang out on the weekend, you know, studying normally going to move once in a while," her dad. Julie's face began to show signs of suspicion.

"Is that not okay?" Max asked

"Yeah, it's fine," she replied. "I'm just a little surprised is all."

Max took a sip of his soda. "I'm not going to be attending Bible study anymore."

"Wow. Does it really bother you that much?" Julie asked.

Max nodded.

"Then I understand," she said. A few seconds passed and she added, "Jenny is going to miss you."

Max nodded, but then saw the devious expression on Julie's

face. "What do you mean?"

"Nothing," she smirked. "She's just going to miss you."

"I'm sure she will," Max said. "We both started at the same time, so we were both the newcomers."

"Yeah, that's it." Julie continued to smirk.

"What are you getting at?"

Julie looked at Max with her eyes wide open. "She has a crush on you."

"Oh, I don't think so," Max said, his line of sight moving from Julie to the table as if he was trying to figure this out. "Do you think so?"

"Of course I think so," Julie laughed. "I'm the one who just said it."

They each went back to their drinks and sat in silence for a few moments.

"Wait a minute," Julie suddenly snapped. "Is that what all the 'we can do other things together' was about?"

Max nodded.

"Why did you feel like you had to tell me this way, you know, that you had decided to stop going to Bible study?" Julie asked.

Max shrugged. "The last time I mentioned not coming back, you used that to get me to continue. You said I should keep going for no other reason than I get to see you there."

"What?" Julie was shocked. "Are you saying I used a guilt trip? I most certainly did not."

Max was stunned. Did she really not remember?

Now it was Julie's eyes that shifted back and forth as she searched her memory. "Oh my gosh. I really did, didn't I?"

Max smiled as if to offer amends.

"Sorry," she whispered with a grin.

Noticing the clock, they each got up to go to their 11-o'clock class. They said their goodbyes and turned to go in different directions. Then Julie stopped, cocked her head sideways, and turned back around.

"Hey!" she yelled.

Max, who had already gotten about 40 feet away, stopped and turned back around also.

Julie had a big smile on her face. "You could have just admitted you're gaga over me."

"I guess so," Max conceded. "But you're smart. I knew you would figure it out."

***

The rest of the semester went smoothly. Julie had explained to Professor Nowak and, when Max did meet him in the halls, he always smiled and gave a friendly wave to Max.

A few weeks later, Julie was at the main auditorium on a Saturday. She carried a stack of papers in her arms. It was registration for the next semester, and she was again working as an administrator. She noticed it was about 25 minutes before 8:00 a.m. so she had time to drop off her forms at her computer and grab a cup of coffee. She walked into the auditorium and immediately saw an all-too-familiar scene that made her laugh. The room was completely empty except for one person standing in the line – Max. She set the papers beside her computer, took a seat and looked at her friend who stood there sheepishly.

Max shuffled his feet and stared at the floor to keep from looking Julie in the eye. He was afraid she would burst into laughter any moment. Seconds kept ticking away, and Max began to tap his feet and look all around the room as if nothing was pressing.

Julie shook her head and motioned for him to come on up. "Come on; I haven't got all day."

Max smiled and walked up and handed her his list.

"You are a piece of work. You know that?" Julie couldn't help but make fun of Max's dedication to getting into Physics 101. "Let's get you signed up for Professor Nowak's class."

Max gave her the list and she typed it in.

"All set," Julie said.

Max thanked her and joined her for coffee until she had to return to her registration duties.

He was finally signed up for Professor Nowak's class. He wondered what the Near Impossible Assignment would be. He knew what some of them had been in the past. He witnessed the one about walking on water and Rollo had filled him in on the one about propelling a sheet of paper 300 feet. Others he had learned about were using a single two-by-four, screws, and an empty two-liter soda bottle to make a car that would propel itself at least 50 feet on water pressure, standing on four eggs without breaking them, and propelling a grape through a sheet of tin.

He could only imagine what his assignment would be.

11

Max finished the semester with straight As, which included four classes: The Bible and Western Culture, A History of Judaism, World Religions, and, of course, College Algebra.

Over Christmas break, Julie had decided to go home and spend it with her family. Max was surprised how much he missed her.

But the Maxwells had plans of their own. Max and his mom and dad made their regular annual trip to spend Christmas with his dad's brother, Oliver, who lived in Columbus, about 80 miles away. Oliver was also a man of the cloth, the head pastor of a large Presbyterian church in Columbus. He had never married and had no children, but his home was designated as Christmas central. It was the center location since his dad's sister lived an hour south of Columbus.

His dad's sister, Mary, made up for the lack of kids for the brothers by having five of her own, ages six to 14. Her husband was not a religious man, so he had long since stopped attending the family Christmases here, but Mary made the trip with all five kids in tow.

Max had always enjoyed Christmas time with his family, especially his cousins, all of whom were younger than he. But this Christmas was different. He played with the kids, helped with dinner, and went through all the motions as always, so it was doubtful that anyone else could tell this Christmas was any different at all for Max. But the difference wasn't visible; it was in his mind. He couldn't stop thinking about the Bible study classes with Brad. He couldn't stop thinking about Brad's dad and his seemingly wrong teachings of the Bible. He couldn't stop thinking about Professor Nowak's class and wondering what near-impossible task with which he would be presented. And mostly, he couldn't stop thinking about Julie.

Julie texted Max a few times during the day, mostly to wish him a Merry Christmas. Each time, he returned the text and sentiment.

After Christmas dinner, Max's dad and Oliver drove to the store to pick up some ice cream for everyone. When they returned, they were covered with snow.

Mary turned on the TV to catch the latest weather forecast. Everyone watched, as the report was not good. The storm had gotten worse, and they were talking of closing all the major roads by nightfall.

The reverend thought they should be going, but Max's mom was worried they would get caught right in the middle of it.

"I got plenty of room here for everyone," Oliver offered.

So the decision was made to stay the night and drive the next day. Mary had to call her husband to let him know, and the kids were happy to spend more time with Max.

Max was happy, too.

When it came time to go to bed, Max's parents got one spare bedroom, and Mary and her three youngest got the other. Her two older kids, both boys, got to share the living room with Max. This, of course, led them into trouble, as they kept disturbing the adults with their laughter, which prompted the reverend to get up and threaten to make them sleep outside if they didn't allow anyone to get some rest.

This made them laugh even more.

Finally, they all got to sleep, except Max, who lay on the sofa with his mind still racing. Eventually, at about 2:00 a.m., he gave up and sat up and grabbed the TV remote. He activated the mute as soon as the TV came on so as not to disturb anyone.

His uncle had all the cable channels and Max liked surfing to see what was on. Back home, they had a simple antenna that got the four basic networks. As he scanned through the long list of available channels, he came across an old episode of Bill Nye the Science Guy. He laughed to himself, wondering how Bill would fare in Professor Nowak's Near Impossible Assignment.

Then something else caught his eye. The channel above the one showing Bill Nye listed this as the current program: *FFY ministries*. Max moved the bar upward and looked in the upper right-hand where it gives the details of the programming. It read, *Faith for You Ministries, Inspiration, Arthur Clavin delivers his sermon to his church in New York.*

Max clicked the 'select' button. As the programming filled the screen, he recognized Arthur Clavin right away from his website. And he noticed Brad was right; the church and the congregation were enormous. He searched the remote to find the caption setting since he didn't want to disturb anyone with the volume. He found it and activated the captioning, then sat back and read what Arthur Clavin was saying.

'People keep talking about Jesus being
about love and peace, and I'm wondering what Jesus are they talking about?
Jesus said himself that he came not to
bring peace but a word. Some people
only understand one aspect of Jesus, but
Jesus was about wrath and judgment also.
Some Christians feel like they have to
try to be nice all the time and try not
to offend anyone, but that's crazy. The
gospel should be offensive. If I go
somewhere and preach and people come up
to me later and say they were offended,
then I praise God that I did it right.
We have to deliver the Word of God like

```
a hammer hits a nail. We don't have
time to be polite. It's like the Bible
says - we are the salt of the world. Let
me explain what that means. If you rub
salt into an open wound, it stings. It
hurts. That's why we are the salt. We
are to throw ourselves into the world
with a fury and make it hurt. That's
what we're called upon to do. We are
at war. Paul tells us to don the armor
and be prepared for battle. We are at
war against the nonbelievers and we will
prevail."
```

Max sat there with his bottom jaw dropped. As the programming broke away for a commercial break, a standard disclaimer appeared:

```
The views of this programming do not
necessarily represent the views of this
network.
```

Good call, thought Max. *They don't represent my views either.*

Max couldn't believe that someone would take metaphors from the Bible and try to make them read as if they weren't metaphors. When Jesus said he came not to bring peace but a sword, it was a symbol of the division that could be caused by some accepting Him and some not. It had nothing to do with an actual sword. The same when Paul talked about putting on the armor of God — it was a metaphor. Unless somehow a person believed that the belt of truth, the breastplate of righteousness, the shield of faith, and the helmet of salvation were all referring to actual pieces of equipment to strap onto your body. Even in that scripture, it mentions the "gospel of peace." How could someone think that meant war?

And the Salt of the World parable was one of Max's favorites.

Matthew 5:13: "You are the salt of the earth. But if the salt loses its saltiness, how can it be made salty again? It is no longer good for anything, except to be thrown out and trampled underfoot."

It had always had one simple meaning to Max. It meant that Christians were the pure of the world. But what happens if a Christian loses his faith? They are no longer able to spread the faith and are now no different than other men. This was the first time he had heard anyone give an alternative meaning to that wonderful parable and it bothered him.

Max watched as the programming came back on with an address for where to send your donations. He turned off the TV and tried to go to sleep. But still sleep shied away from him as if he were trying to trick sleep into getting closer, but sleep knew it was a trap. So he lay there wondering how someone could preach these things and how so many people could follow these teachings.

He understood now why Brad embraced conflict over reason. The Faith For You website was full of messages about war and conflict. Now Max had seen his first TV broadcast and, ironically, it mentioned war as well.

Max had always struggled with his views on war. Every Christian he knew, including his father, believed that you should support war if it was a just war in defense against an evil aggressor. Max had even tried to embrace this belief, but when he really thought about it, he realized the only wars he supported were those led by the United States, and it made him wonder if they did indeed hold a monopoly on justice. He knew that when people decide for themselves what is just, who is evil, and what constitutes defense, it leaves a lot of room for personal prejudices. In the last decade, it had been suggested that preemptive attacks are considered defensive acts. Max knew it was easy to let your support of the troops translate to support of the war, and it was the only time he worried that his Christian values might not lead the way. He often wondered if his patriotic views took precedence.

Max knew that the word "war" was only mentioned 14 times in the New Testament, and seven of those times are in Revelation talking about things like the war in Heaven. Of the other seven places it is mentioned, three places are in Matthew, Mark, and Luke, which mention wars and rumors of wars. Two other places mention war against the mind and soul. One place is Jesus telling a metaphor about a king going to war. The only one of the 14 that seemed to be providing insight to Christians about their stance on war was 2 Corinthians 10:3 where Paul wrote, "For though we live in the world, we do not wage war as the world does."

It was very confusing to Max. But one thing he was certain of was that war was not something to promote and embrace as the Clavins seem to do. It might only be mentioned 14 times in the New Testament, but when Max did a search on the Faith For You website, he found it listed over 2200 times.

Between Brad and his father, Max began to realize that everything they taught seemed to cater to basic human instincts. The message seemed to be that you are one of the chosen ones so you're set; you won the lottery; you found the last Golden Ticket. The other people, those who were not chosen, don't have it and never will. What's more, there's nothing they can do to get it. Since you're one of the chosen, you are supposed to be judgmental, you are supposed to be aggressive and offend people, and you are supposed to be about conflict and war. If someone strikes you on the right cheek, make them pay for it.

Finally, it became clear to Max. That's the reason that Clavin's message was accepted by so many. It required no discipline or sacrifice at all. Max had always believed that what separated a Christian from everyone else was devotion and sacrifice. It's not easy being a Christian and the Bible never said it was going to be. In fact, the Bible says the opposite. As a Christian, you are called upon to rise above all of the emotions, shortcomings, and weaknesses of the human condition. But now, along came pastors like Arthur Clavin, and they tell you that it's okay to be all of these things, that you've been granted salvation no matter what. The more Max thought about it, the more he understood the appeal. That would sound great to anyone.

Now Max understood why Brad was so gung-ho and borderline militant. That's why he chose conflict over compassion, friction over union, justification over joy. Brad accepted his father's philosophies 100% and parroted them in every Bible study session Max had attended. It was like they took bits and pieces of scripture, certain words from certain passages, and entire metaphors, to completely ignore the simple teachings of Jesus, to reinvent the message from Christ to fit their own personal views.

And people ate it up.

Max finally understood.

12

Max walked into Professor Nowak's class for the first time. The room was an auditorium-style room with seats that lined up in slightly curved rows, with each row of seats set higher behind the one in front. There were three aisles, one on each side and one in the middle, that led up between roughly 12 rows of seats. Opposite the seats was a one-foot-high platform in front of a double-sliding chalkboard and a science lab-style desk about five feet in front of the chalkboards.

The room was located in the older building and had wood walls and even a ceiling made of wood. It was all correlated with a burnt umber finish over beautiful walnut wood, although the finish had long lost its luster. There were no windows at all — only three doors: the main entrance, a door on the opposite wall that appeared to be the professor's office, and an emergency exit at the top of the center aisle.

The ceiling was high and, along with the walls, consisted of designs and carvings that left crevices and ledges that had long since foregone dusting. The air above head level was old and stagnant and, combined with the smell of old wood, gave the room an odor that seemed all too familiar to Max. It smelled like a church.

Max had hoped to get a seat up front, but was surprised to see the room already mostly filled. He ascended the middle aisle and found a seat by the aisle about seven rows up. Along the right side of the seat near the aisle was a small desk platform that manually rotated up, which provided an area on which to place your books.

The room was abuzz with obscure chatter, quiet laughter, and feet shuffling.

As the clock hit the top of the hour, Professor Nowak entered from his office door. He wore dark pleated slacks and a sports jacket over a white button-up shirt, which displayed a slender tie coming from underneath the neatly pressed collar. He took his place behind his desk and began.

"OK, settle down, everyone. Let's get started. I have a list here of people who are supposed to be here. I will read it off and, when you hear your name, you will say, 'Newton.' If you do not hear your name, it is a distinct possibility that you are lost." He began to read off the names without looking up. One by one, students rattled off the word 'Newton' as their name was called.

"Johnny Maxwell," the professor called out, looking up from the list for the first time.

"Newton," Max said and raised his hand as well.

The professor smiled and continued. After he completed the list, he set a cardboard box upon the desk. "OK, class. It's good to see so many new faces. The bad news is, if you are taking my class early in your college career, I am added to inform you that it's all downhill from here."

Low but very audible laughter filled the room.

"I know most of you have no doubt heard," the professor continued, "that every semester I provide you with a chance to pick up bonus points for your grade. I assure you that most of you will need it. This bonus comes in the form of what has been dubbed 'The Near Impossible Assignment.' It was originally called 'The Impossible Assignment,' but since several students have actually succeeded, the name just didn't seem to fit anymore. This year's assignment is going to take a lot of balls."

This made the room fill with much louder laughter, even from Max who was excited to hear the assignment.

The professor reached into the box and brought out a round metal ball. "These balls are made of lead. Your assignment, should you choose to accept it, is to make this ball magnetic. You can do anything you want to the ball as long as at the end of the semester it can be picked up by this very strong magnet." He held up a magnet about three inches long, an inch wide, and a half-inch thick. He scanned it over his desk, and paperclips and even a ball-point pen leaped to attach themselves to the magnet.

Max looked on in amazement.

"Nothing can be attached to the ball at the time of the test," the professor continued. "It doesn't even have to be in a spherical form at the time, but it must consist only of lead. You cannot add anything to it."

Max had waited so long for this moment. Now it was here and it did indeed seem like an impossible challenge. He couldn't wait to get started.

The professor stood at the bottom of the seats and held the box for anyone who wanted to try it. Over 75% of the students filtered down to grab one, each with the same smile Max displayed, perhaps each thinking they would be the one to pull it off.

As the class progressed, Max could barely concentrate on the subject matter as Professor Nowak scribbled on the chalkboards and even showed the students a slide show. It was the bulge in his pocket, a simple lump of lead, that kept succeeding over and over in capturing his thought process. *Why is lead not magnetic?* he asked himself. *How do you make it so?*

It was late Thursday afternoon when Max got home from the first day of class of his second semester. He didn't have to work so he rushed through his homework so he could get on the computer and research questions that had plagued him the better part of the day. As the internet slowly came on, he typed into the search bar, "Why is lead not magnetic?"

Several pages came up and Max began to scan through them all. Finally, one read:

"Lead is not magnetic because it does not have electron spin. For any metal to be

magnetic, it must produce an electronic
angular momentum to interact with the
magnetic field."

OK, thought Max. All I have to do is get its electrons to spin. He then laughed at the absurdity of it. But he continued to research. He read up on electrons, electromagnetic fields, and electricity. They seemed to all correlate. He read that you can take electricity and run it through wires wrapped around an iron rod and it would turn the iron magnetic. But that wouldn't work with lead. Or would it? It seemed like the best place to start.

Max walked out to the barn with his lead ball in hand and a large flashlight from the pantry. The barn had one light fixture that operated by pulling a string, but it did not illuminate the far reaches of the building. Looking around, he found a roll of plastic-covered wiring. That, along with the six-volt battery from the flashlight, was enough to run his first test.

Wrapping the wire clumsily around the lead ball, he attached one end to the positive terminal of the battery and the other end to the negative. He took a nail and touched it to the ball.

Nothing.

But the nail gave him another idea. He placed the lead ball in the vice of his dad's drill press and located a drill bit that was the same size in diameter as the nail. He drilled a hole right through the middle of the ball and was surprised at how easy it was to drill through a soft metal like lead. Taking the nail, he tried to slide it through the hole, but it was a tight fit so he took a hammer and drove it through until two inches of the steel nail protruded from each side of the lead ball.

Max placed the ball on the table and began wrapping the wire around the nail instead of the ball itself. Then, he hooked it up to the battery again, took another nail, and placed it on the ball.

Nothing.

He tried placing the nail on the wire-covered nail, which ran through the ball, and the nail latched on in a magnetic embrace. So the premise of the electromagnet was sound, but it only worked with metals already magnetic. Max shook his head.

Just then, he heard his dad's truck pull into the driveway. He walked out to the front of the barn entrance and waved. Puzzled, his dad walked to the barn to see what Max was up to. His dad was wearing work clothes with no coat, even though it was winter and quite chilly outside, so Max knew right away that he had been on a plumbing job.

"What are you doing out here, son?"

Max explained about the assignment and what he had read on the internet. He explained how his first experiment had failed.

"Using a flashlight battery, huh?" his dad asked in obvious interest.

Max nodded.

His dad continued. "What happens if you use a stronger battery?"

Max smiled. "It says it will make the electromagnet stronger."

"You don't say." His dad turned and went to his truck, went into a side compartment, and took out some tools. He opened the hood of his truck and worked a few minutes, then headed back to the barn with his truck battery hanging by the handle in his right hand, swaying in rhythm of his arm movement as he walked.

Max couldn't help but grin at his dad's enthusiasm.

The reverend set the battery on the table and hooked up one end of the wire to the positive post on the battery using a small clamp. He grabbed a set of vice grips to attach the other side. He then stopped and motioned for Max to take over.

Max stepped up and took the vice grips and, as he placed the other end of the wire to the negative battery post, he said, "Here goes nothing."

He and his dad looked on for a few seconds until Max took a nail and again lay it on the wire-wrapped nail. It grabbed on harder this time. He pried it away and then touched it to the lead ball.

Nothing.

He looked at his dad, smiled, and shrugged his shoulders. "Good idea anyway," he said.

Something caught their attention as they looked at each other and simultaneously crunched up their noses. There was an unmistakable tickle to their olfactory senses, a familiar twinge in the ozone that takes a few seconds for the brain to recognize. In unison again, they looked back at the lead ball. Smoke was surrounding the plastic-coated wires. It was dense smoke that hovered instead of rose, but was starting to spread.

"Oh shoot!" cried Max, and he grabbed the wire and pulled it off the battery without loosening the clamp. As he unwound it from the nail, it was obvious that the plastic had begun to melt. As he peeled back the layers, the plastic coating went from being soft to smoldering. He quickly unraveled it all to reveal burning embers. Max leaned down and did the only thing he could think to do — blow real hard. It worked. That was the blast of oxygen the embers needed to ignite and that's what they did. Flames appeared like ghosts to dance in the air above the wires.

The reverend walked over to the other track of the barn and picked up a plastic five-gallon bucket, which had originally held sheet rock mud but had for years been sitting right outside the barn door collecting rain water as if for this very moment. He carried it in deep and dumped the entire contents into the table, extinguishing the fire.

His dad looked at him and then back at the mangled mass of exposed wire and charred coating. He looked back up at Max and said, "That reminds me of the one and only rule I have for this experiment."

"Don't burn down the barn?" Max asked with a wry smile.

His dad simply touched his finger to his nose, then picked up the battery and took it back to his truck. After he got it reinstalled, he closed the hood of the truck and went into the house.

Max stayed behind to clean up the mess. The entire table and surrounding floor were soaked with the stagnant rain water.

He casually unwound all the burnt wiring and discarded it into the now empty bucket. As he stared at the lead ball with the nail through it, he began to doubt his approach. *Should I go back to the drawing board?* he wondered.

Then, he smiled as he remembered a lecture in high school about successful people who refused to let adversity and failure stand in their way. One of his favorite stories was of Colonel Sanders and his idea to peddle his family chicken recipe to restaurants across the country. When asked how many rejections he had received before the first restaurant said "yes," Max had answered ten. He and the others in his class, were shocked to learn it was over 900.

When he put it into that perspective, one little barn fire was nothing.

13

The following Monday, Max could not stop smiling as he drove to college. His failure at the Near Impossible Assignment and subsequent near fire were pushed aside for more favorable memories, even though his dad kept reminding him of the other.

Julie had driven over to attend church with Max and afterward had eaten lunch with him and his parents again. Like the first time, it was a very nice experience, and it was clear that his mom and dad liked her very much, and it would seem they liked that he liked her as well.

Church and lunch made up a tiny portion of his memory, however. It was after lunch that consumed his thoughts this morning as he replayed every detail in slow motion. After lunch, Max's parents left to visit a sick elder of the church, leaving Max and Julie there alone. Before leaving, Max's mom had already dug out several old pictures to embarrass Max and Julie kept that going after she left. They looked through his school yearbook and several family albums.

"I'm glad you asked me to come," Julie said.

"I'm glad you came."

Several seconds of silence followed and Julie asked, "Have you ever thought about kissing me?"

Max felt his throat tighten. He knew Julie was outspoken and he loved that about her, but this question suddenly made him dizzy. But he managed to answer honestly. "More times than I can count. And I'm pretty good at math."

Julie smiled a really big smile. "Then why haven't you?"

Max shrugged. "I've never kissed a girl before, and I was scared that I would be really bad at it."

Julie never tired of hearing honest responses from Max. But she couldn't help but have a little fun at his expense. "So you think there's a wrong way that will make a girl not interested in you anymore?"

"Well," Max said as his brow lowered, "I actually thought there were a million ways to do it wrong that would lose the girl and only one right way, and I have no clue how that goes."

Julie decided she had picked on him enough. "OK, I'm going to make it easy for you."

Max breathed a sigh of relief.

"Close your eyes and leave your lips open. For the next ten seconds, don't do anything at all; just let me do everything."

Max did as he was instructed. Julie moved the picture albums and sat across Max's legs with her own legs resting on the sofa cushions. Max's heart was beating very fast. Suddenly, he felt Julie's lips on his, slowly brushing against them, and then both of her lips were on his bottom lip. She slowly compressed her lips, creating a slight vice-like grip on his bottom lip and pulled away, taking his lip with hers and then slowly released it. She continued this all around his bottom and top lips. Max felt like he was in paradise. He never knew he could feel this way, and he hoped that those ten seconds would last for eternity. His eyes were still closed, and his mind was still flowing when he realized that it had stopped. He opened his eyes to see Julie leaning back and smiling at him.

"How was that?" she asked.

All he could do was nod; the rest of his muscles seemed frozen. "Should I be doing something?" he asked.

"Believe me," Julie replied, "doing nothing already makes you a better kisser than 90% of the men out there. Trust me."

Max looked confused. "How many boyfriends have you had?"

Julie smiled. "One, back in tenth grade, and we never kissed. All this is from what I read." She paused for a few seconds. "OK, this time keep your eyes closed, but try to mimic what I did before."

Max quickly closed his eyes. As Julie's lips touched his, he began to open and close his lips on hers. He was concentrating so hard in the beginning, but his mind slowly became a void as his lips caressed hers with more and more passion. His arms drifted up to caress her back, and his head tilted instinctively to create a better angle in which to embrace her mouth fully. His mind was as far away from his fears and reality as they could be. Only when Julie moaned in pleasure did he snap out of it. He opened his eyes as they pulled away from each other.

There was no smile on Julie's face. Her lips still parted and eyes still half-closed conveyed that she too was fully swept away in the moment.

"Holy moly," was all she could mutter.

Max nodded in slow motion to concur.

"You are a great kisser," Julie said as she sat up straight and tried to regain he composure.

I'm a great kisser? Max thought. I'm a great kisser?

Julie leaned over and put her arms around his neck and placed her face against his chest, the back of her head up against Max's cheek.

I'm a great kisser? Max thought.

***

The gravel on the side of the road jumped up to impact the bottom side of Max's truck, creating an almost machine-gun effect.

"Whoa," Max said as he came out of his hypnotic state and eased the truck back into the lane. He realized he better concentrate on the road for the remainder of the trip. That lasted for about seven seconds as his mind wandered back once again to where his mom and dad left the house.

He arrived on campus and went to his first class. He couldn't wait to meet Julie for their 10 a.m. regular cafeteria get-together.

Finally the class was over. He and Julie sat side-by-side at the small table. Neither had gotten anything to eat or drink this morning, as it seemed the important thing was simply to be there. As they sat and whispered, they were interrupted.

"What's wrong with this picture?" Rollo said rubbing his chin.

"You're not in class?" Max guessed.

"No, no, that's not it," Rollo continued. "Hmmm, what can it be? Wait, I got it, you two are not sitting across from each other like normal. Wow. What can that mean?" He sat in the chair opposite them and placed his elbows on the table and formed a V with his hands where he settled his chin. Then, he looked at them with quick blinking motions as if awaiting an answer.

No answer came.

"Oh," Rollo said, giving up, "I'm happy for you guys." Then he looked at Max. "You're hot as fire, dude."

Max smiled.

Rollo continued. "And we all know fire is what makes things magnetic."

Max's mouth dropped open as he spun around to stare at the only person who could have betrayed him. "You told him?"

Julie giggled. "I saw him when I came back Sunday night and it just slipped out."

Max laughed, too.

"How was church service with Max this weekend Miss Blankenship? Meet the future in-laws?" asked Rollo.

"It was great," Julie replied. "Max teaches Sunday School to these small kids. It's too cute. They call him Mr. Max. Then, when the main service started, his dad…"

"No, no, no," Max said placing his hand over Julie's mouth. "You've done enough damage."

Rollo was laughing now and wasn't sure why. "Come on, spill it."

Max finally conceded and removed his hand.

"OK," Julie began, "His dad came out and walks up to the podium and looks out over the congregation. Everyone is expecting him to start on his sermon, but he does something else instead. He says, 'I realize that I have been negligent in my duties as far as your safety goes so let me take a moment to correct that. Please take a moment to familiarize yourself with all emergency exits in case of a fire.' Max's face was so red. He just sank in the pew, and people were laughing and patting him on the back."

"Now that's a fun place to go to church," Rollo said, shaking with laughter.

"Those weren't his exact words. That sounds more like what they say at the movie theater." Max's attempt at diversion failed and they continued to laugh. He couldn't help but laugh himself.

"Oh, did you guys hear about Brad?" Rollo asked as if he couldn't believe he just remembered.

Julie and Max both shook their heads, waiting for him to continue.

"He had a wreck."

"That red little Porsche?" Julie asked.

Rollo nodded.

Max looked confused.

"Haven't you ever noticed that black Porsche 911 parked right by the main entrance?" Julie asked Max.

"Yeah but I thought it was a teacher's. Isn't that the teacher parking spaces?"

Rollo rolled his eyes at Max's innocence. "The almighty dollar, dude," he said, rubbing his fingers across his thumb to signify money. "His dad went to school here and donated the entire science lab."

"That's good," Max replied. "Everyone should do good things if they have the money for it."

"Right. Jesus was all for tax write-offs." Rollo shook his head to make sure the less-than-subtle sarcasm was understood.

"Well, is he alright?" Max asked. "What happened?"

Rollo turned his hand up to mimic holding a bottle while letting his tongue hang out of his mouth. Not the level of a professional mime performance, but good enough to get his point across.

"Drunk driving again?" Julie blurted out.

Max couldn't believe it.

Rollo noticed the look of shock in his face and said, "Dude, this is like the fifth time."

"But he's okay?" Max asked again.

"Yeah, he's fine," Rollo finally answered. "He's with his dad in New York while his dad smoothes things over again."

Max got that Rollo was not that concerned, but he couldn't help but feel really sad for Brad.

After the hour was up, they said their goodbyes and went off to their respective next classes. For Max, it was Professor Nowak's class. He walked in to the auditorium-style classroom and started to ascend the middle aisle to assume his seat. He stopped, however, as the professor walked out of his office and called out to him. Max turned to walk back to the professor.

"I need to talk to you," Professor Nowak said.

"Sure," said Max.

"Well, the thing is," the professor continued as he worked his way around the back of his desk and Max moved over to the front, "I have a very important task to assign you. I usually designate one student every semester for this assignment and it's very important."

Max wondered what it could be, but felt honored that he had been chosen.

The professor went on. "First, I want you to understand that this is a volunteer position, and you should feel free to turn me down if you don't want the added responsibility or think that it might in some way take away from your focus on the subject matter."

Max was completely enthralled.

The professor could sense his curiosity so he drew it out

even longer. "I have others I can ask if you are not interested."

"What is it for Pete's sake?" asked Max.

The professor smiled. "These old buildings are a hazard so we need someone trustworthy to be in charge of this." He pulled out a small fire extinguisher and handed it across the desk to Max.

"Julie?" Max asked shaking his head.

"Actually, it was Rollo," the professor corrected.

Max reached for the extinguisher, but the professor pulled it away to signify it was only a joke. Max turned and went up the steps to his seat, knowing his dad would be pleased at how many miles this silly joke had tallied.

14

Max had not given up on his approach to the assignment. Manipulating the physical structure of the lead ball and hopefully getting the electrons to spin was still the goal. He had upgraded the coated wire to the thickest, most heavy-duty he could find for the size needed. In addition, he now had it set up to run an AC current through the nail itself, hoping that that would generate some effect. He did this by cutting one strand of an electrical cord from a lamp and connecting it to one side of the nail, then continuing it on the other side of the nail back up to the lamp. When the lamp was turned on, he knew that the current would be flowing directly through the lead.

It had been three weeks since the fire episode. As Max pulled into the driveway of his family's home after driving home from school, he noticed a box on the door stoop and hoped this would be the thing he had ordered to progress to the next step of his experiment. His dad's truck was gone, and he realized that his mom was also not home, meaning they were either shopping or visiting friends, which is why UPS had left the box at the door. He read the sticker on the box and quickly opened it to reveal two small devices about four inches high, two inches wide, and two inches deep. They resembled two little speakers, each with electrical cords protruding from the rear.

Max had read online that microwaves are actually electromagnetic waves and thought that also might have an effect on the electrons of a metal. But as he looked at the two emitters, he noticed that they were different. He wasn't sure why one had a radiation warning on it and the other didn't. The emitters were not supposed to generate enough power to be dangerous. Taking the one with the warning, he flipped it upside down to read the label on the bottom.

It read: *Beta emitter.*

What did that mean? Max went up to his room, got on the internet, and searched for "beta emitter." What he read shocked him. Beta waves are high-energy, high-speed electrons emitted in certain types of radiation.

Radiation? Oh no, Max thought as he wondered if this was even legal. He looked up his invoice where he had ordered these online to make sure he hadn't made a mistake. But his records confirmed that he had placed the order for two identical microwave emitters. He looked up the website again and searched to try to find a contact number to let the company know they had sent the wrong item. He couldn't find a number, but there was an email address. He opened an email box and began to compose the letter. Then, he stopped as the definition echoed in his head. *High-speed electrons*

Max looked at the little seemingly harmless unit in his hand. He concluded that the least he could do was give it one test run before sending it back

It was early February and snow was on the ground as he walked out to the barn. The barn offered little protection from the cold, but at least it was dry inside. Max took the two emitters and placed them on each side of the lead ball. Then, he connected them to a large rusted metal box, which was placed on the old wooden table near the lead ball.

Years ago, Max had found an old electronic amplifier in the basement of his dad's church. His dad said it was there before he took over and thought it was used at one time to regulate the signal of either the microphone or organ speakers. Max had rigged it to regulate the power of both the DC current going through the coated wire and the AC current going through the nail. After connecting the two emitters, everything now ran through the homemade regulator.

He decided to give it a quick run before his parents got home. He turned on the power and rotated the knob on the front of the amplifier in a clockwise direction from its starting position to about the 1/10th mark. The light of the lamp began to burn very dimly. Max looked at the lead ball with all the wires and two emitters on each side as it sat in the black circle created by the fire. He carefully touched a metal nail to the lead ball.

Nothing.

He turned the dial a little more to the right and the lamp shone brighter. He tried again.

Nothing.

He turned the dial to almost the halfway mark. As he did, he heard the sound of an automobile and walked over to the entrance of the barn to notice his dad's truck. He figured he best stop the experiment here. He had to get ready for work anyway. He walked back to the table, but the ball was gone and there was a hole in the table. He then noticed the ball on the ground; the coated wiring had unraveled on one side as the ball had fallen to the ground, and on the other side the wire had broken as the ball went through the table.

Max stared in disbelief. How had this happened? Had the fire damaged the wood on the table and weakened it enough to break through? He looked at the hole, but the wood of the table seemed normal below the surface. In fact, it was an old homemade work table, and the top consisted of three-quarter-inch plywood. It would take a great force to punch a hole in that.

Max cut the power completely and just left it all like it was. He walked into the house to greet his parents and get ready for work.

***

Max placed several boxes of different items on his dolly to wheel out to the floor. But his mind was elsewhere. *What had happened to the lead ball to make it break through the table?* As he neared the two swinging metal doors that led to the retail floor of the store, he stopped. The bottom of the doors had three-quarter-inch plywood attached to them to protect the metal from the impact of dollies from employees and vendors. He had always noticed that, but never paid any attention to it before. As he stood there motionless, Mr. Mitner walked up behind him.

"The automatic doors are only at the front of the store," he joked.

Max smiled and then asked, "You see that plywood on the doors there?"

Mr. Mitner looked confused, but nodded.

"How much force would you think it would take to punch a hole in plywood that thick?" Max asked.

"Is this one of your college problems?" Mr. Mitner asked as he shrugged.

Max nodded.

"Well," Mr. Mitner began, genuinely trying to be of assistance, "it would take more than I could muster. I mean, I don't know what kind of pressure in pounds per square inch or anything like that, but I'm certain I couldn't knock a hole in it with a hammer."

"Wow. You're right." Max began to realize the gravity of what had happened in the barn.

Mr. Mitner seemed glad that he could offer some insight. Then, he added, "And I'm sure your dolly won't hurt it if you decide to put those items on the shelves where they belong."

They both laughed as Max agreed, pushed the doors open, and continued to work.

The rest of the evening was the same. Max went through the motions, but couldn't stop thinking about what had happened. He considered several possibilities. In trying to manipulate the electrons of the lead, had he instead compromised the molecular structure of the wood underneath? One thing was certain — he had to find out.

***

It was barely daylight as Max walked out to the barn. He had set his alarm clock for an hour earlier than normal so he could run the experiment again, but, hopefully this time, without distraction. It was freezing and he was bundled up pretty good, but could still feel the cold penetrating his clothes.

He took off his gloves to work, which made it colder. He reattached the broken wire and rewound the other side. He set everything up about a foot away from the hole in the burnt area and tried it again.

As he turned the dial clockwise, the lamp began to brighten. As he neared the midpoint, the point where he had gotten to before, he could see that the ball was starting to sink into the first layer of the plywood. He couldn't believe it. He turned it just a little more and heard a crack as the plywood started to break underneath the ball. Max turned the dial back to the starting position. He wasn't sure what was happening, but felt it was significant. Then he had an idea.

Max looked at his watch to see the time. He still had about 30 minutes before he had to leave for school, so he ran to the house and went inside to the bathroom. He returned to the barn with his mom's bathroom scales.

He placed them on the table and set up everything on top of the scales. The manual scales barely registered the weight. As he slightly turned the dial on the amplifier, however, it jumped up to the twenty-two pound mark.

Oh my gosh, Max thought. One of his theories was correct. The experiment had made the ball heavier. As he slowly turned the dial, the weight increased exponentially. By the quarter-way mark on the dial, the scales were pegged out at 250. Max decided to take it a little further, but as he did, he noticed the ball was beginning to dent the top of the scales and backed off.

But now he knew. He didn't understand why, but at least he knew what was happening. Instead of making the electrons spin and hence making the lead ball magnetic, it was somehow causing the molecules of the lead to get heavier. Or maybe it did have to do with a magnetic solution. Maybe the experiment was causing the lead ball to react to the earth's gravitational pull in a magnified manner, hence the effect being similar to gaining weight.

As he stood there in the freezing air pondering the possibilities, he knew now that making the ball magnetic was no longer important. That meant, of course, that his dream of succeeding in one of Professor Nowak's Near Impossible Assignments, a dream that began on his first visit to Cedarbluff's campus, now took a backseat to the accidental results of the experiment. He wasn't sure of the ramifications of what was happening, or even clear on what good could come from such a discovery, but he knew he needed to pursue it to see where it would go.   And he couldn't help but wonder how increasing the power using the amplifier would affect the weight of the ball, but he was dying to find out. He also knew he would have to figure out another way to set up the experiment since the proverbial table to clearly was not able for his super weighted ball

But that would have to wait.

15

Valentine's Day fell on a Tuesday, and Max had made sure to have that day off from Hurley's Market. It was 6:00 p.m., and he sat at the Red Lobster in Fort Wayne, Indiana with Julie, Rollo, and a girl named Rita. This was the first double-date he had ever been on. In fact, it was the first date period.

Julie had begun to attend church with Max every Sunday, which always led them to find a place to be alone afterward. It was a great time for Max, as his feelings for Julie were very strong. But he still wasn't sure if they were boyfriend/girlfriend or even how that distinction was determined. As was typical, he hoped that she would clarify it for him one day. In the meantime, he was very happy.

Rita seemed to Max to be very nice. Like most of the girls who gravitated to Rollo, she seemed to giggle at everything he said. She was physically very pretty, and he was still surprised that someone Rollo's size could date such pretty girls. But all he had to do was spend a little time with Rollo to understand because it was never a dull moment around him. He usually made your sides hurt from laughing so hard.

"A toast," Rollo said as he raised his glass of soda.

Max and the two girls lifted their glasses of soda as well.

"To the coolest friend anyone could have," Rollo continued looking straight at Max, "the Mormon pyromaniac."

Julie laughed. Rita laughed too, but wasn't sure why, so Rollo explained what had happened with Max's experiment.

"How's that going by the way?" Rollo asked.

"Yes?" Julie chimed in, realizing that she didn't even know. "How is that going?"

"I think I'm there," Max replied. Seeing the 'good for you' expressions and nods from the group, he added, "I think I have officially reached the point where I know for sure that this is impossible."

They all laughed.

"Are you serious, dude?" Rollo asked.

Max nodded. "Maybe not impossible, but at least beyond my ability."

Rollo offered his condolences. "That's okay, man. Welcome to the loser club. You still have a lot of redeeming qualities." Rollo paused and stared into the air for a few seconds. "I'm not sure what they are, but I'm sure you have some."

The atmosphere was great and Max enjoyed the company of his friends. He had never had really close friends through high school. He knew everyone, but because he didn't play sports or wasn't in the band or didn't take part in any extra-curricular activities at all, he never had at kind of bond with his classmates. Being a devout Christian might not have helped with the "in" crowd either. But he felt lucky to have these guys at this point in his life.

After dinner, Julie rove back to Max's house with Rollo and Rita in the backseat, usually making out, which embarrassed Max and disgusted Julie. She looked over at Max and asked "Why haven't you told me about the experiments and how they're going?"

"I don't know," Max replied.

"But you were serious; you don't think you can do it?"

Max nodded. "Yeah, I was serious."

"You still have a lot of time left in the semester," Julie pointed out. "So keep trying."

"I'm going to keep working on it," Max said. That was an accurate statement. In fact, in a rare move, he had taken a full Saturday off from work to devote to it. Julie had decided to go home to visit her parents this coming weekend, so Max had decided he would spend the entire day seeing how heavy he could make a simple ball of lead.

***

Max looked over his odd contraption. It was set up and ready to test. He had replaced the nail with a longer steel rod. All the coated wiring had been replaced. Years ago, his dad had installed a 220-volt outlet for a welder, so Max now had a 220-volt industrial heater instead of a 110-volt lamp to pull the electricity through the rod. The two emitters were positioned as before, but now the entire thing was set upon a one-inch iron plate, which was about eight square inches in size and set directly on the ground.

Max took a deep breath, which the cold air turned into mist as he released it. He began to turn the dial clockwise on the amplifier, and the coils in the heater began to illuminate. He slowly turned it more. As he neared the halfway point, the iron plate seemed to sink a little into the ground or maybe that was just his imagination. He turned it more. The heater brightened and the iron plate seemed to strain under the pressure. Max turned the dial even more, now a little past the halfway point. The iron plate seemed to cry out from the stress. It was not really audible, but more a sense of unimaginable pressure. It gave Max the feeling of turning a stuck bolt with a large wrench and knowing that any minute the bolt would break. Max noticed that the ball was starting to indent the iron plate. Was that even possible? Maybe the ball itself was flattening. His nerves were on edge knowing that something bad could happen any minute, but he couldn't resist turning the dial more.

Suddenly, the experiment was halted as both emitters fell over onto the ball. Max didn't know what had caused it, but assumed the stress of the iron must have caused them to fall over due to the vibration. It took Max an hour to figure a way to mount the emitters to the plate. But finally it was ready and he tried again.

He passed the halfway mark with the same effect as before. When he reached the three-quarter mark on the dial, the ball shot off the plate. It happened so fast that Max didn't even notice which way it went. But now he could see that the iron plate had indeed been dented from the weight of the lead ball. This meant that not only was the ball getting heavier, it was becoming more solid.

Max killed the power to the amplifier and walked around looking for the ball. He couldn't find it. He noticed no trails in the dirt to show where the ball had rolled, which meant it must have gone airborne. But surely Max would have heard it hit the walls or any of the other stuff in the barn. He started to get frustrated as he considered the possibility that the experiments for today were over, and he would have to ask Professor Nowak for another ball. Desperate, he tried to retrace possible ways the ball could have gone. As he looked back at the place of origin, there sat the ball on the iron plate as if it had never moved, the wires still in place.

He shook his head. Between going to college, driving back and forth, working, going to church, doing homework, spending time with June and this experiment, he had begun to seriously cut into his free time. But had seeing deja vu vision cause him to hallucinate. Had the ball been here all the time. It couldn't have been. Never in his life could he ever see the indentation before.

Max slowly walked back over to the amplifier, keeping his eyes on the ball as if it might jump up and run away just to taunt him. He turned the amplifier back on and began at the far left position again. He passed the midway mark and kept his full attention on the ball. If he felt he needed to blink, he waited to resume. As he neared the three-quarter mark, he watched intensely as he sensed the iron straining once again. One more little turn and it happened again. But this time, he knew the ball did not leave the plate, it was simply invisible.

Several seconds passed before Max realized that his mouth was wide open. Could this be real? He could see the wires, and this time he even noticed that the steel rod was still visible, but its color had blended in with the iron plate so he hadn't noticed it before. Everything was still there in its place except for the lead ball itself. It was without a doubt invisible.

Max slowly turned the dial backwards and it reappeared. As he turned it back more, the less stress it seemed to put on the iron plate.

Then he had an idea. With the power switch off to the amplifier, he set the dial to the three-quarter mark, the farthest point he had turned it to so far. Then, he flipped the power switch to the "on" position and the ball disappeared again. No straining of the iron, just poof! It was gone.

He walked around the barn trying to get a grip on what was happening. Just then he heard his mom calling out to him. He noticed that it was already 5:00 p.m., and he had been out here most of the day. He decided to call it quits and walked into the house.

His mom and dad were just sitting down to dinner, so he went into the bathroom and washed his hands. He came back, took his seat, and after his mom asked the blessing, he began to eat in complete silence. His mom and dad didn't notice how deep in thought he was, or if they did, they didn't mention it.

After dinner, Max talked to Julie on the phone for a long time, then sat and watched TV with his parents for a short while. At nine o'clock, he decided to go on to bed.

As he lay there in bed, he knew he wouldn't soon fall sleep. What had he done? What should he do now? Although this seemed like a great discovery, what possible applications could come from it? Max closed his eyes and tried to imagine, but the only visuals he could come up with were military uses. He pictured the government building new planes that could become invisible, making it easier to bomb other countries.

He cringed at the very thought.

He wasn't sure what time he had fallen asleep, but he knew it was very late. The sun was shining bright through his bedroom window, and he knew right away he had overslept. He jumped out of bed and ran downstairs. His mom and dad were already gone.

He looked at the clock. It was almost 11:00 a.m. He had missed church. That had never happened. He was frantic. Then he saw the note on the bathroom door.

```
We thought you needed the sleep, so we
didn't want to wake you. We are picking
up Mrs. Johnson and Dad said Ryan could
teach your Sunday School class today.
Please get some rest, and we'll see you
when we get back home.  Love, Mom.
```

Max was relieved, but he still felt bad for missing church. However, it gave him time to address the source of his sleepless night. After a glass of orange juice, he went back out to the barn.

He decided to get it over with and go for broke. He set the amplifier to the full farthest-right setting. He stood back behind a support beam, then took a garden rake and reached over to flip the switch to the "on" position.

Flip.

The heat came on and the ball appeared again, same as before. The ore didn't seem to be any different. He walked over and turned the amplifier off and the ball appeared.

'What am I going to do when you have asked you and

16

Professor Nowak sat behind the desk in his office and stared across at Max. He was surprised to see Max waiting outside his classroom very early this Monday morning, but that was nothing compared to his confusion now. "It gets heavy then disappears?"

Max nodded.

The professor smiled. "I don't think weight and invisibility go hand in hand. If it did, we might lose Rollo." He laughed at his own joke and leaned forward to glance out the door, half expecting Rollo and/or Julie to come in laughing.

Max was expressionless.

"You are joking, right? I mean this is payback for the fire extinguisher, isn't it?"

Max was expressionless. Then he said, "I understand you think this is a joke. But even if you think that, you agreed at the beginning that you would not tell anyone about this. You gave your word."

"Let me get this straight," the professor said, finally getting serious. "You're telling me you can make the lead ball disappear? Invisible? As in, it's there, but you can't see it?"

Max nodded.

"But that doesn't get you any points with the magnetic challenge," the professor noted, trying one last time to keep it light-hearted in case it was a joke.

Max just sat there wondering if he had made the right decision.

The professor recognized his frustration. "What do you want me to do?" he asked.

Max breathed a little sigh of relief. "I would like you to come to my house so I can show you I'm not crazy."

"OK," the professor said. "When?"

"I'm off Wednesday night," Max said.

The professor agreed, but, deep down, he still thought it might be a setup.

Max left his office and began his day. He tried to put the experiment out of his mind and concentrate on his studies, which had taken a back seat as of late. And he tried to concentrate on Julie, who was also starting to feel a little neglected.

***

Professor Nowak pulled into the driveway at Max's parents' house at a few minutes after 5:00 p.m. Wednesday evening. Max had been watching from the window and walked out to meet him. After a casual greeting, he led him out to the barn.

"Ready, was? the professor gasped as Max gave him a couple redo the experiment and progressed, nudging having to commit the minutes to keep them firm mind. "OK, so what. Do you think."

Max recreated the experiment the entire scenario, he started to explain what he was setting and proceed once he was over. When he reached the point, the professor could sense something was happening. Then, like all the other times, the ball disappeared before their very eyes.

Professor Nowak jumped back and screamed, "Holy crap!" Then he stepped a little closer, his eyes transfixed on the void where the ball used to be.

"Like I said," said Max, "you can still see the metal rod and everything except the lead ball."

Several seconds expired as the professor was at a loss for words. He couldn't take his eyes off the phenomenon. "And you say if you crank it up even higher, there's no change?"

"Correct."

"Have you tried to touch it to see if you can actually feel it there?" asked the professor.

Max answered, "I thought about it, but since there's 220 volts of electricity passing through that visible rod, I thought better of it."

Professor Nowak reached inside his coat and took a pen from his shirt pocket. He leaned in, inching the pen toward the rod. He was about two inches from it when the pen slid out of the cap and disappeared into the void.

Max cut the power as he and the professor looked for the pen, which had not reappeared with the ball. "What just happened?" he asked.

"I have no idea," the professor acknowledged.

As they were scratching their heads over the pen, Max's dad walked in. "Hey, guys. How are you doing?"

"Oh, hey, Dad. This is Professor Nowak, the teacher I told you about."

Max's dad walked over to shake his hand. "Very nice to meet you, sir."

"The pleasure's all mine," said the professor. "Max here talks about you all the time."

His dad laughed. "Well I assure you I'm not as bad as he claims. It's freezing out here. Why don't you guys come in the house for a while? Max can teach you how to build a fire later."

The professor laughed while Max rolled his eyes.

They went into the house and sat at the kitchen table. The professor was introduced to Max's mom who insisted he stay for dinner. The professor agreed.

"Do you need some help?" the professor asked.

Max's mom spun around with a big smile. "Did you hear that, guys?" Her rhetorical question was clearly aimed at Max and his dad. Then, she turned her attention back to the professor. "No. But thank you so much for asking."

As Max's mom continued to work at the counter, Max's dad took his opportunity. "I have to be honest and say that we were a little worried in the beginning when Max suddenly developed such a fondness for science. You do realize that a lot of pastors think that science leads a lot of young people away from God?"

The professor nodded. "Yes, I am aware of that. I wish it weren't true because I think science and Christianity go hand in hand. I don't see them as enemies at all. In fact, it was science that brought me to God."

Even Max's mom paused at those words.

"Really?" asked the reverend. "That's an interesting view point. Can you explain how that happened?"

The professor looked upward as if wondering where to begin. "I've always been fascinated with science, ever since I was a kid. But the more I learned, the more I realized it couldn't be just coincidence. The fact that the earth is the perfect-size planet and the perfect distance from the perfect-size star is a huge coincidence in itself.

"The scientific theory about the moon is also fascinating. They believe that another planet or asteroid collided with the earth at just the perfect angle to tip a piece of it away to form the fe - size moon, which is located the exact distance wa... The moon's gravitational pull keeps the earth tilted at the perfect angle to keep the earth from wobbling like the other planets and that this allows - son we have four seasons and the only reason our vitamins stable enough for life.

"Then there's the whole water theory. Do you know that scientists believe that meteors rained down on earth for millions of years, bringing tiny droplets of water until they formed the oceans, lakes, and rivers? How did it happen on earth and no other planet?

"Science even favors the Bible when it comes to mankind. They have found primate skulls going back millions of years. They can see where these skulls have changed over time, but they are still primates. Then, for some reason that science can't explain, there is a very long period of time with no skulls being found.

Then, suddenly, human skulls appear. So the link doesn't appear to be missing; it would appear not to exist.

"Throw in things like the miracle of birth, the human body, and especially the human brain, and it was things like that which made me realize that there had to be intelligence behind it all."

Everyone in the room had stopped to listen, even Max's mom. And everyone was impressed, even Max's dad.

"So you don't think the earth was created in six days?" his dad asked.

"I don't know," the professor offered, knowing this was sometimes a touchy subject for Christians. "I think Genesis was kept simple for us to get the gist of creation. I don't think Moses, or even Einstein for that matter, could ever comprehend the complexities of an infinite being like God. I don't think we were ever meant to fully understand how it happened, and maybe our minds could not ever fully understand it."

Max's dad moved to his next question. "How about evolution?"

The professor smiled and threw his hands up. "No, no. That's definitely one I steer away from."

His dad smiled. "Why is that?"

"Because," the professor answered, "people get too upset when discussing that."

Max finally spoke. "You don't have to worry about that with Dad. He can disagree without getting upset."

Professor Nowak thought back to the Bible study classes where Max had admitted that he and his dad didn't see eye-to-eye on some subjects. Judging by that and his dad's expression, he decided to take a chance. "OK, then. What about evolution?"

"Do you believe in evolution?" his dad clarified.

"Of course," the professor began. "That's like asking if I believe in gravity. It is not a matter of believing; evolution is real and all around us. If you plant a garden, the plants evolve throughout the entire process. Take Max here. I'm sure he didn't look the same ten years ago."

"That's aging," his dad tried to correct.

"Yes," the professor agreed. "Aging is a form of evolution. Evolution simply means change in a certain direction, so aging is a perfect example.

"Another example would be animals found in the Amazon that have long tails to survive the six months when the Amazon basin is flooded. The same species are found in other parts of the world with no tails at all."

"That's adaptation," the reverend said, as if rolling out his ammo already selected for this conversation.

"Yes," the professor agreed again. "Adaptation is also a perfect example of evolution."

The reverend went for the kill. "OK, let me clarify. I'm asking if you believe that guy, Darwin, and his story that man came from monkeys."

"No, of course not," the professor replied. "But let's be clear; Charles Darwin never said that."

Max's dad looked confused. "Are you sure?"

The professor nodded. "I know people say that all the time, but it's not accurate. Al D in v ly ot e d s h m nd n le sh e a c n a ce o . i c e A m nd n le is 7 er l. n l s t re s f he e . d s 't m e ec y r , ca in le ta hy h th e s . S w p op e s c w ar t ic e till ha gin nt n , i s ue, co ir g ha s D wi hey e e d ."

Max's dad was at a loss for words. After a few seconds he asked, "But you do believe that man has evolved over time? Correct?"

"Yes," the professor answered.

"But how can you say that when the Bible says that man was created in God's image?"

"I believe they were. Adam and Eve lived in a paradise, which means the weather was perfect and everything was provided for them. I suspect they were very beautiful people. But when

God kicked them out of Eden, they were then subjected to freezing cold and had to hunt for their own food. It doesn't make sense to me that God would not have given man the ability to adapt since he gave it to every other creature on earth. It just doesn't make sense to me. So maybe they adapted, which coincides with science. And, as we are able to control our own environment with houses and buildings with controlled temperatures inside those houses and buildings, maybe we are slowly changing back to what Adam and Eve must have looked like. But we'll never get there because our man-made environment will never equal God's paradise."

Again the room was silent until Max's dad spoke. "Would you like to come speak to my Sunday School class?"

Realizing he was serious, the professor said, "I'd love to if I ever have the time."

Max's mom put dinner on the table, and they all ate and conversed about simpler subjects. After dinner, the professor thanked her for the meal and thanked Max's dad for the discussion and invitation. They bade him farewell and Max walked with him as he left the house.

"You have a nice family," the professor said.

"Thanks. So what do you think about the experiment situation?"

"Well," the professor smiled, "I certainly don't think you're joking anymore. And I think you're right; we should keep this to ourselves until we figure it out."

Max nodded in agreement.

He got into his truck and drove away, but he couldn't help thinking about the lead ball and the invisibility concept. It didn't make sense. And what happened to the pen? These thoughts kept crossing his mind as he drove to his house, which was located near the campus. Suddenly, he slowed down and pulled over as if even driving was a distraction. He looked in the rear-view mirror at his own reflection. "No," he said.

Back at Max's house the phone rang. His mom answered

and called out to Max.

"Hello?" Max said.

"I got it. I figured it out."

"Professor?" Max asked.

"Yes, it's me. I figured it out. Can you come in early to-morrow and meet me in my office?"

Max wanted to know now, but knew it was best to wait. "Sure. No problem."

"What's up?" his dad asked, as Max hung up the phone.

"Oh," said Max. "Professor Nowak lost his pen."

17

For the second time this week, Max walked down the ghostly dim hallways of Cedarbluff in the early morning hours. Tall windows cast odd shadows, which drifted along the high walls of the corridors as if they were dark angels watching silently from their perches. Not a soul was present, not even a custodian, as Max could hear the rubber soles of his own shoes compressing against the polished tiled floor, before the shuffle of students' feet and the sound of voices would drown out everything else.

The door to Professor Nowak's classroom was open. Max walked inside and followed the path to his office, which was also open. Walking in, he noticed the professor scribbling on a notepad and, upon noticing Max's presence, he abruptly looked up and motioned to him.

"Hey. Come in. Come in." The professor jumped out of his seat and came around the desk, looked out his office door, then guided Max to his seat. "Let me go close the door."

Max watched as the professor walked back over to the classroom door, looked outside both ways, and then closed it. His demeanor, Max thought, was that of a secret informant, worried that the bad guys were closing in. It made Max a little uncomfortable.

"OK. OK," the professor said as he walked back into the office. "Uh, let's close this door too."

As he closed the office door, Max really began to get anxious.

The professor took his seat and started to speak, but instead got back up. "You know what, let's keep this door open so you can watch the front door." He got up and opened the office door again and sat back down.

"You're starting to freak me out," Max said, being completely honest. "What's going on?"

Professor Nowak finally settled down and looked directly at Max. "Do you know what you've done?"

The words caught Max off-guard. They scared him.

"Look," the professor continued, "forget about invisibility. That's not what's happening here. OK, look here." He grabbed his notepad, but stopped and looked out through the office door. "OK, come here."

The professor walked out to the chalkboard and Max followed, still feeling uneasy about this whole meeting. The professor began by drawing a line on the chalkboard.

"If you have a one-dimensional line, right? If one spot on that line becomes too dense. . ." The professor began to take the chalk and vigorously rub on one spot of the line. ". . .that the p[rop]er[ty] o[f] the [fi]rs[t] di[me]n[s]or ca[n't] b[e] l[on]ge[r] [su]pp[ort] it, [it] fal[ls] o[u]t [o]f [t]h[e] fi[rs]t dir[m]en[s]ior a[n]d n[o]t e[xp]ec[ted]." [H]e t[hen took] the[c]ha[lk] a[nd] [d]r[e]w a [li]ne fr[o]m his s[po]t [to] be pe[rpen]dicul[ar] to [the] li[ne] crea[t]ing [a shape]. [He] [the]n [th]en [t]urne[d] t[o] [l]o[o]k at M[a]x [with] c[o]n[ce]rn [that he] w[a]s fo[llo]vi[n]g.

[Ma]x [n]odde[d]. ["O]K[, I]'[m] [w]ith y[o]u."

["G]oo[d,]" th[e] p[r]of[e]ss[o]r sa[i]d [a]s [h]e [r]an [to] t[he] [c]las[sr]oo[m] door again to make sure no one had entered. Next he drew what looked like a flat diamond shape. "Now if you have a two-dimensional plane and one point becomes too dense for the properties of the second dimension to support it. . ."

". . .It falls out of the second dimension into the third," Max finished the sentence as the professor drew another perpendicular line starting at his point on the plane.

The professor erased the line and plane examples without even looking at Max and drew a box on the board. Placing his next dot inside the box, he turned to look at Max.

Max was staring in amazement.

The professor nodded. "If a point in the third dimension becomes too heavy to be supported by the properties of the third dimension, it falls…" He took the chalk and drew a dotted line from the dot inside the box straight across until it was outside the box.

At least ten seconds of silence passed as the professor allowed what he was saying to sink in. "That's right, Max. Your little ball is not turning invisible. It's completely visible wherever it's at. Or I should say *whenever* it's at."

"Is it possible?" was all Max could mutter.

"It all makes sense," the professor reasoned. "The ball gets many times heavier each time you increase the power even a little. As you increase the power a lot, it becomes so heavy that it literally falls out of the third dimension into the fourth — time. That would also explain why the emitters were drawn toward it and why my pen was sucked into the void left by the ball. It's Einstein's theory of wormholes."

"You're talking about a black hole," Max said. "It can't be. Black holes are strong enough to suck in entire galaxies, let alone felt tip pens."

The professor smiled as if he had already considered that. "But black holes in space begin as supernovas, which are a thousand times larger than our sun. Compared to our little lead ball, they're a hundred billion times greater in mass to begin with. They get denser as they collapse and all that mass gets compressed into a relatively small area. But you have found a way to make the molecules of lead heavier without changing its physical size. So our little ball cannot suck in an entire galaxy."

Max began to accept the professor's explanation. "Do you think it's going forward or backward in time?"

"I don't know," said Professor Nowak honestly. "But there's a chance that someone is walking along, past or future, and your ball appears on the ground."

128   Reternity

Max suddenly became concerned at that possibility. "Could it shock them or electrocute them if they tried to pick it up?"

"I don't think so. The connections all stay in our time. It looks as if only the lead ball itself travels, so that's all that should show up in another time."

The professor's words were a little comforting, but not entirely. "What if they pick it up and break the connection?" Max asked.

"Good luck picking it up," the professor laughed. "It would weigh so much they couldn't lift it."

Max was confused again. "I assumed it would be back to normal wherever it appeared."

"Whenever," the professor corrected. "No. It travels through time and loses weight as it travels. The farther it goes, the less it begins to weigh. Just like hitting a baseball. The original force propels the ball, but it slowly loses that momentum as it travels and falls to the earth. If it didn't, it would go on forever. That's the basic law of force. Once the weight of the ball becomes low enough to be supported by the third dimension, it falls to earth, so

os ea Tl s a s n ar t a y u re nc cor t that ere re
o a es on givn t e a o g p wer d ppe to v-
g f po er h v   o b th h yc gi it f po er.
ou e the a u c f rt i ti e '

is s t u a ," M x ai   s ery in ega to nk
. W t a we alki g al u re "

e p of s o m le . 'We re t kin ab t th N el Prize. We're talking about the National Academy of Science. We're talking about the John J. Carty Award, the Daniel Giraud Elliot Medal; we're talking about every major award in science. This is the most important discovery of the 21st century. No, wait: this is the most important discovery in the history of mankind. You're going to be more famous than Einstein."

This was too much for Max as he walked over to the front row of seats and sat down.

The professor erased the board as if the crude drawing itself would give away everything then walked over and sat next to him. "What are you thinking?" he asked.

"It's over," Max replied. "I have to stop the experiment now."

"What? Why?" The professor was shocked.

"It just doesn't feel right to me. I don't desire fame and I don't see how this discovery could help mankind."

"What about disease?" the professor reasoned. "What if we could go forward in time to bring back medicine that could cure all the ills of today? What if we could go back in time and find cures for today's ills, cures that might have lived in animals that have long gone extinct? The possibilities are endless."

"Would not bringing back medicine from the future destroy the future as it exists?" Max asked.

The professor couldn't answer. He knew Max had a point. "It's your decision, Max. It's your discovery. I'm just an observer."

"Let me think it all over," Max suggested. "Don't get me wrong, I'm as blown away by this as you are. I just want to be sure we do the right thing. Unfortunately, I can't recall any scripture at all that mentions time travel."

They both laughed and Max got up. "I guess it goes without saying that we need to keep this to ourselves for the time being."

The professor nodded as Max left him sitting in the front row of his classroom.

***

"Are you on another planet or in another time zone?" Julie snapped.

"Oh, sorry," Max replied as he realized his mind was indeed somewhere else. He began to talk with Julie again and tried hard to push back the events of the meeting in Professor Nowak's classroom.

It had become customary for Max and Julie to sit in Max's truck on Friday after their classes were over until the last possible minute before he had to leave to get home and change for work.

"What has you so preoccupied anyway?"

Max shrugged. Then, he decided to see if he could get another point of view without revealing anything. "Have you read *The Time Machine*?"

"H.G. Wells? Yeah, a long time ago. Why?" Julie asked.

"I've been thinking a lot about that story recently. He used the time machine just to explore really. He did try to help those little people in the future, but he didn't really seem to try to help the people of his time."

"How do you mean?" Julie asked, now as intrigued by where this was going as she was intrigued as to where it was coming from.

Max continued. "I mean, he didn't try to discover medicines or technology from the future and bring them back to share with the people of his own time."

"That's true," Julie acknowledged. "But wouldn't that have altered the future if he did that?"

"I guess that's the real question. I guess if you really travel in time you could only do it as an observer and not get involved in anything."

Julie nodded.

Max began to stare out the front windshield, and Julie saw that she was about to lose him again.

"Hey, stay focused."

Max smiled and continued the discussion. "It would be cool to go back in time to witness dinosaurs and stuff."

Julie looked as if she was losing interest in this conversation. "I guess so," she muttered.

"I'm sorry," Max offered. "Let's change the subject."

"No, it's okay," Julie replied. She really didn't want to have this conversation, but if it was the only way to have any conversation with Max right now, she was willing to give it a try. "Yes, it would be cool to go back in time to see dinosaurs and stuff. Yes, it would be cool to go forward in time to see how advanced we have become, providing we haven't killed ourselves off by then."

"Do you think we have the ability to do that?" Max asked.

"I don't know. But I know we have the destructive nature to do it."

Max thought about what Julie was saying and knew she was right.

Julie smiled at how seriously Max was taking this conversation. "Are you planning on time-traveling anytime soon?"

Max laughed. "No. Not anytime soon."

Julie added, "But let's be honest. If we could travel in time, it would not be medicine or technology we would be after."

"It wouldn't?" Max asked. "What would it be?"

"Lottery numbers."

18

Max began to feel a little weird standing outside the professor's classroom very early on a Monday morning yet again. It marked the third time in eight days.

As he awaited, even dreaded, the professor's arrival, his mind drifted back to elementary school and the only time he had ever gotten into trouble. Mrs. Birch, his fifth-grade teacher, had sent him out into the hall to wait for the principal for pulling a little girl's hair. Max was not the guilty party, but decided accepting the punishment was more honorable than being a stool pigeon. That same feeling he had then of impending doom mixed with a leaping dose of anxiety was the same feeling he felt now.

It was his first uneasy feeling since Friday night, which began like so many others recently with too many things running through his mind, like a carousel spinning out of control, and sleep was just an innocent kid trying hard to figure out a way to hop on. But what made his night different was that Max had finally made a decision and that decision comforted him. The carousel stopped and sleep took over.

On Saturday morning, he stood in the barn ready to implement his decision. The hammer came down hard on the first emitter, breaking the casing and sending shards of plastic in all directions. The second blow completely separated the casing and the exposed inner mechanics were no match for the third and fourth blows, which made the remains unrecognizable, much less operational. The second emitter suffered a similar fate.

Max scooped up all the little pieces and took them, along with the lead ball with the metal rod wrapped in plastic-coated wire, and deposited them in the trash receptacle out by the side of the road. Then, he went back into the barn and disconnected everything from the amplifier and stacked it neatly in a corner of the barn.

He breathed a huge sigh of relief.

Since he still had an hour before he had to leave for work, he decided to go back in and cook breakfast for his mom and dad. Twenty minutes later, the smell of bacon and eggs filled the little house as his mom and dad wandered into the kitchen with stunned expressions.

Max turned and handed them both a cup of coffee, each already prepared the way they liked it, and then turned back to the stove.

"What's gotten into you?" his mom asked after taking her first sip of coffee.

"Don't jinx it, honey," his dad said with a smile.

Max knew he better say something or they would keep on asking. "I just got a good night's sleep and feel brand new."

"Finally starting to get used to all these hours you've been putting in?" asked the reverend.

Max nodded as he set the bacon on the table.

They sat and had a great family breakfast together until Max left for work.

The rest of his day was the same; it seemed everyone at work could sense that he was more focused, attentive, and seemed to be his old self again, and it carried over through Sunday.

Sunday after church, Julie and Max sat watching TV until his mom and dad left to visit members of the congregation. As they went out the door, Max and Julie embraced. He was still too embarrassed to kiss her in front of them.

"Wow," Julie said, pulling back with a surprised look on her face. "Where did that come from?"

Max smiled as if he didn't know what she was talking about.

"What's up?" Julie pressed. "You seem to be in a good mood for a change."

"Have I been in a bad mood?" Max asked.

"Well, not necessarily. But you sure seemed out of it lately, like you've been really stressed."

Max smiled. "Well, I apologize." He leaned over for another kiss.

"Not so fast," Julie teased. "What's the deal? Why were you so distracted for the last two weeks? Oh wait, did you figure out how to make lead magnetic?"

"No," replied Max. "I didn't solve anything; I just finally accepted something."

"What does that mean?" Julie said with a frown. "Are you giving up? I thought succeeding in Professor Nowak's Near Impossible Assignment has been your goal since you visited campus."

Max nodded. "But I didn't like how it was taking my attention away from the really important things in my life. Like. . ." He leaned in again and this time Julie obliged.

As they paused, she laid her head upon his chest. "Since you seem to be your old self again, there's something I've been wanting to ask you."

"What's that?"

"Well," Julie started off slowly, "you know Brad is not coming back this semester. They're letting him finish a correspondence-type program from home. Since it was the friction that bothered you and also the others giving you the big head for taking on Brad, and that was the reason you didn't want to come to Bible study anymore, well that is no longer a problem."

She paused at that subtle segue for Max to take over. He did not so she continued. "So will you start coming to Bible study again?"

Max wasn't sure what to say, as he wondered if the professor would even want him to come or even want to keep him in his class. He wasn't sure how he would react to his decision about the experiment. The best he could do was to tell Julie he would think it over.

* * *

"I'm going to have to give you a key."

Max looked up to see the professor walking toward him and smiling. He unlocked the door, and they entered the classroom and he invited Max to join him in his office.

"Wow." That was the only thing the professor could say when Max told him of his decision.

"You're not angry?" asked Max.

The professor was still speechless as he looked down at his desk, and you could tell from his expression and eye movement that he was still trying to let it all sink in.

"Professor?"

"Huh? Oh, no. No, no. Of course, I'm not mad," the professor finally said as he realized his thoughts had lured him away from the conversation. "I told you it was your decision and I stand behind you. Wow. You really are a man of conviction."

The professor's smile finally put Max's nerves at ease. They sat and talked and joked around for another 30 minutes. They parted by shaking hands, and Professor Nowak reminded him that he would see him in Bible study Thursday night.

* * *

Rollo smiled and got out of his chair as Max and Julie entered the student center for Bible study. Rollo threw his hands out in the air and started bowing in an exaggerated movement. "We're not worthy. We're not worthy."

Julie clenched her lips and gave him an evil stare, which Rollo recognized right away.

"Kidding with you, dude," he said, shaking Max's hand. "Glad to have you back."

Max noticed that all the same people were there, including Jenny, the girl who had started the same day he had. His old seat seemed to have disappeared, as Jenny and Rollo now sat beside each other. Julie's seat across the way was still there and empty. The only other empty chairs in the circle were beside Professor Nowak, which is where Brad and his girlfriend had been sitting. Max was relieved. He half expected a monitor to be there with Brad joining them via conference.

The professor motioned for them to take those seats, which they did.

"OK, we're all glad to have Max back," the professor began. "Let's begin with Trish. Your topic was about salvation. Remind us again what it was."

Although he never caught her name before, a girl who had been there during each of Max's visits spoke up. "My question was: When we die, if we are awarded eternal life, will we go to Heaven right away or only after judgment day?"

She paused to look back at the professor who added, "Go ahead. Tell us first what you believe."

"Well I can only go by what our preacher says. He says the spirit goes right away to be with his Lord, and the bodies are ... te a judgment ... by eternity – either eternal punishment or eternal damnation.

Professor Nowak held up his 3 ... and tapped the cover with his fingers.

Oh yeah, Trish said, looking back at her notes. 'Luke 23:42-43."

Another one of the ones that Max didn't know by name was first. He read, "Then he said, 'Jesus, remember me when you come into your kingdom.' Jesus answered him, 'Truly I tell you, today you will be with me in paradise.'"

"2 Corinthians 5:6-8," Trish added.

Julie was first. "Therefore, we are always confident and know that as long as we are at home in the body, we are away from the Lord. For we live by faith, not by sight. We are confident, I say, and would prefer to be away from the body and at home with the Lord."

"That's about it," Trish concluded. "He said all of Revelation 20 and 21 also."

Just like before, slight nods of agreement circled the room. Just like before, the professor asked if everyone was in agreement. And just like before, all eyes instinctively turned to Max.

Max looked out over the group with a sudden auspicious familiarity. "It is Revelation that makes me think the opposite," he began. "I think we mentioned this verse before when talking about faith and deeds. Revelation 20:13."

Everyone started flipping except Julie who just seemed happy that Max was here.

Jenny read, "And the sea gave up the dead which were in it; and death and hell delivered up the dead which were in them: and they were judged every man according to their works."

"I see you have a Kings James Bible tonight," said Max.

Jenny blushed. "I couldn't find my NIV."

"No, that's good," Max comforted. "That helps me make my point. This is talking about the dead being called back to be judged after the thousand-year reign. When the Bible was translated into English from Greek, the word 'hades' got translated to 'hell' most of the time. Yet hades only means grave. This is one of those verses that really shows that. But in the NIV, it has been translated back to hades."

Everyone was now on the verse, and you could see their heads tilt as they verified what Max was saying.

"So," Max continued, "if you go by the King James version, it makes it sound like you went to Hell before you were judged. That doesn't make sense, does it? If a person lived on earth for 70 years, did everything right according to the Bible, and was certainly going to be rewarded eternal life, why would they first have to endure 1000-plus years living in Hell and being tormented by Satan?"

Max looked around the room, making eye contact with

those not still reading the verse to make sure everyone was following. The nods and smiles gave him that confirmation.

"So following that same train of thought, according to what Trish has said, or her preacher has said, if a person has lived 70 years and intentionally ignored the Bible and maybe even killed, raped, stole, et cetera, then when he dies he will go to Heaven to be with God for the next 1000-plus years before his body is called back to join his soul and be judged."

The room was completely silent.

"I just don't think that will happen either," Max continued. "I think you are judged once, and that is to determine between Hell or Heaven or at least between eternal life and eternal death."

Kenneth smiled a really big smile. "Max is no longer a Mormon. He's now a Jehovah's Witness."

Light laughter filled the room, which grew in intensity as Max asked, "Really?"

When the laughter died down, Max added, "It's just that wherever the Bible mentions going to be with the Lord after you die, none of the places say it is immediate except when Jesus told [the guy ... on the cross he would be with him in paradise ... have ... Maybe he ... is made a special arrangement for him. Maybe not. Maybe we could go straight away. I don't have the answers; I'm only telling you what I read from it.

"... you believe our bodies and our souls were for 1000 years ... be called back together?" asked another one whose ... are N... the dead ... never remember ...]

"I don't know about our bodies," said Max. "The Bible says the dead will be called back. And notice that it says hades and the seas will give up their dead. If a person has been buried for 1000 years or died at sea, then there would be no body as we know it. And why would our bodies need to be judged when they are only vessels? It is our soul that is judged."

Everyone sat there pondering Max's words.

"Do you have other scripture to back up your views?" asked the professor.

Max thought for a second. "1 Thessalonians 4:13-17."

Trish was first. "Brothers and sisters, we do not want you to be uninformed about those who sleep in death, so that you do not grieve like the rest of mankind, who have no hope. For we believe that Jesus died and rose again, and so we believe that God will bring with Jesus those who have fallen asleep in him. According to the Lord's word, we tell you that we who are still alive, who are left until the coming of the Lord, will certainly not precede those who have fallen asleep. For the Lord himself will come down from heaven, with a loud command, with the voice of the archangel and with the trumpet call of God, and the dead in Christ will rise first. After that, we who are still alive and are left will be caught up together with them in the clouds to meet the Lord in the air. And so we will be with the Lord forever."

"Job 14:12."

Kenneth read, "So he lies down and does not rise; till the heavens are no more, people will not awake or be roused from their sleep."

Max concluded, "I think when Paul refers to those who sleep in death, that's what he is talking about. And he says that those of us who are here during the second coming of our Lord will not precede those who have fallen, but the dead in Christ will rise first. So all of this coincides with Revelation 20 saying that we are all called back after the thousand-year reign of Christ, and only then are we judged and only then we will be awarded eternal life or eternal death."

"That makes sense to me," said Trish.

This brought laughter again from the circle of students.

"Wait," said the professor. "He's arguing with you. He's saying you're wrong. How can you agree with him?"

Trish was grinning and even blushing a little. "I'm just saying it makes sense."

The rest of the Bible study session was the same. Max differed a little with others, but they all had a good time discussing their different views. It was a peaceful and serene experience for

Max, one he needed and appreciated.

There was no tension, no bad karma, no yelling, and not once did the professor have to put a stop to the discussion. There was only a shared feeling of joy that seemed to radiate from the circle as if it were an electrical impulse being transferred from one seat to the other as it circled through every student there. This was the feeling that Max remembered from other Bible study groups. He wondered how a Bible study class or any group of people who came together to talk about the Lord could not result in a feeling of joy.

He inhaled deeply as if he could actually breathe the feeling into his lungs. He reached over, took Julie's hand in his, and gave it a slight squeeze as if to thank her.

This is what Bible study should be, he thought.

19

Max sat at the kitchen table with his physics book open. It was three weeks until the end of the semester, and he had an A in all his classes but one — this one. It wasn't that it was harder than he had expected; it's just with all the attention and focus he had placed on the bonus assignment, he had not maintained a solid grasp of each chapter of the text book as the class progressed. And what was now abundantly clear was that keeping up as the problems evolved was at least as important as your ability to understand the material.

As he buried his attention into the book, the phone rang. He heard his mom answer and give the phone to his dad. He could tell his dad was talking to his brother, Oliver, and the conversation seemed serious.

After he got off the phone, his dad walked into the kitchen to get a cup of coffee.

"Is anything wrong?" Max asked.

"Uncle Pete is in the hospital in Tennessee. He had a minor stroke," his dad replied as he took the coffee pot from the platform of the coffee-maker and began to pour the remains into a cup.

"Is that Grandma's little brother?"

His dad looked back at him and nodded. Then, he spoke up so his words could be heard in the living room. "Don't change my channel. I'm coming right back."

Max asked, "Are you going down there?"

His dad sat down across from him. "That's what we're trying to figure out, if I should fly down there." He took a sip of the coffee and made a sour face. Walking over to the microwave, he placed the cup inside and set the timer for 50 seconds.

As Max watched, he suddenly forgot about his dad's uncle as he began to think about flying to Tennessee, the television, the coffee-maker, and the microwave. His dad took out the cup and tested it and found the temperature to be satisfactory and walked back toward the living room.

"Dad, can I ask you a question?"

His dad stopped and looked longingly at the living room for a second, then smiled and came back to his seat across from Max. "Sure, son. What's up?"

"I was just thinking," Max began, "about science and Christianity. I know there seems to be a conflict, especially with certain scientific theories. But how do you feel about technology?"

His dad tilted his head as he thought about that. He took another sip of coffee before answering. "I have no problem with technology. Why do you ask?"

Max thought about how to word his concern. "Well, most technology is either based on science or directly created from science. I know you have flown on a commercial airliner several times, and we have a lot of gizmos around the house, so it seems like science isn't quite the enemy they've might think it is."

"Science has never been the enemy," his dad corrected. "It's men who use science to try to prove there is no God. That's not the problem."

"So you would say that the invention of the airplane is a good thing as far as Christians should be concerned?"

Once again, his dad paused to reflect on the question. "Yes, I would say it's a good thing, possibly a great thing. The invention of the airplane has allowed men to better spread the Word of God; it's allowed people to visit family and friends; it's allowed people to visit sick relatives; it's made it easier to transport medical supplies and even donor organs to get them to hospitals on time. I'm sure I can think of more if I concentrate on it."

"But what about the attacks of 9/11? What about building bombers and that kind of thing?" Max asked.

His dad finally saw where this was going. "Let me ask you this, Max. Do you believe a gun is evil?"

"I believe it was created for evil."

His dad shook his head. "That wasn't the question."

Max thought for a second. "OK, the gun itself is not evil."

"Correct," his dad nodded. "Neither is the airplane or any other invention. It takes a person to be evil, and a person can and will use any device or machine in the world for evil. Should we do away with airplanes and all the good they have done since their creation because someone used one to cause the deaths of innocent people? If airplanes didn't exist, would those people have given up or found another way to carry out their mission of hate?"

Max had never thought about it that way before. As he sat there pondering, his dad figured his job was done and got up and went into the living room.

***

The following Friday afternoon, when Max got out of his last class, instead of sitting in the truck with Julie, they took her car to go to a small diner close to the campus that was a local gathering point for students. Max was not scheduled to work this day because he had a meeting with Professor Nowak at 3:30 concerning his grade.

The professor met with every student who had less than an A-average going into finals to explain what they needed to do to finish strong. Max felt a little foolish to be in this group but certainly didn't want to turn down a chance to figure out what he could do to improve his grade.

"What is your grade right now?" asked Julie as they sat at a table and shared a paper bowl of onion rings and drank a soda.

"81."

"Oh no," Julie joked. "You could end up with a B. Your life will be ruined."

"If I do poorly on the final exam," Max clarified, "it could be worse than a B."

Julie conceded.

When they had finished their meal, Julie drove back to campus. As they got out of the car and went their separate ways, Julie reminded Max to text her as soon as he got out of the meeting.

Max walked the all-too-familiar path to Professor Nowak's office. The classroom door was open and he walked over to knock on the closed office door. After an invitation to enter, he opened the door, walked in and took his seat across from the professor again — a seat he knew all too well.

"81," the professor began abruptly.

Max nodded with a feeling of shame.

"OK, it's not the end of the world," the professor said to lighten the mood. "We still have the final which counts one third of your grade so there's the best way to make a difference. Do you think you're going to be ready for the final?"

"I've been studying hard," Max offered.

"Good. Good. And there's still the bonus of the Near Im-possib e as gr h nt '

M x o e c n u e Ie h; d eve e tiou h o t t again ft r na h d a pe d

Tl p of ss r c ic ii e pi s on. "Yo can s ll pa ti - ate ir t at. Y i kn v I g e o nt i r or gina ty w et e y u uccee t r t.'

'E it .

Professor Nowak anticipated the response and reached into his desk drawer, took out another lead ball, and tossed it to Max.

Max reached out, but missed it as it deflected off his hand and onto the floor beside his chair. They both laughed. Max picked up the ball and realized that things weren't as bleak as he thought.

"Any other things to cover?" the professor asked.

Max shook his head, so the professor got up to walk him out.

"Wait," said Max, then turned around and sat back down.

The professor was stumped but returned to his seat as well.

"There is something else," said Max as he searched the professor's face for a reaction before he even said anything. "I think I made a mistake and I want to apologize."

The professor was still stumped. "For what?"

"About the experiment; I think I was wrong to end it."

The professor couldn't help but smile.

"I'm not saying I want to be involved," Max added, "and I'm certain I don't want the attention that would come with such a discovery, but I think completely ending it was not the right move. What I'm trying to say is that if you want to continue it, you have my permission. That might not be the right word. You have my blessings."

The professor slightly nodded, and it was clear from his expression that he was very grateful for Max's words. The two got up and walked out of the office, and the professor locked the office door behind them. As they walked out the classroom door and started down the corridor, he asked, "You have to go to work?"

"No," Max answered. "I made sure to take today off since I didn't know how long our meeting was going to last."

"So where you headed?" the professor asked.

"Just to hang out with Julie. Why?"

"Well if that can wait about 30 minutes, I'd like to show you something." The professor stopped walking so he could face Max as he awaited an answer. "I live just a few miles from here so it won't take long."

"It's at your house, the thing you want to show me?" Max seemed a little skeptical.

"Yes," the professor laughed. "I'm not going to kill you. You can tell Julie where you're going in case you never come back."

Max laughed. He was right. Why would he have anything to worry about? He texted Julie to tell her he was going somewhere with the professor and would see her when he got back, which should be about half an hour.

The professor led Max to the faculty parking area and to a fairly new Ford truck, a four-wheel-drive vehicle that was raised off the ground a little higher than the factory setting.

Max smiled as he remembered the professor drove a truck since he had pictured him as a sports-car-kind-of guy. He got into the passenger seat and the professor drove away from campus.

A few minutes later, he was pulling into the driveway of a modest brick home. It seemed to only be about 1200 square feet with a detached garage in the back-yard, which the overgrown grass suggested was no longer used anymore. They both got out of the truck, the professor unlocked the door, and they went inside.

Max looked around at the interior décor, which seemed to him to be very normal. There was a small TV set, which sat directly in front of an old torn recliner. The only other seating in the small living room was a ragged old loveseat, which currently held old newspapers and magazines. It seemed the professor didn't entertain much. This also was a shock considering how popular he was and how athletic he seemed to be.

"_____ ar_____ s   h_ p_of s_r _a d _s he _o _ce d M_x
oo__ii_g_ar_   _   _V_n _xp__ti_g som__e t_ j__st
_a__e n_ik

M_x   _   _ _s _re_i_ti_n of tl_t jo__e

"_'s   _   r _ o_ l_ 1 l_a c_ do_ :, _p_r d_t,
_nd p_ _ _e_   t _   s m_n w th_u_ _ai_i_g o_ N_ax

M_x   _____ p_ _e_o. t_rn_d _n _ _igh., _hi_h illu-
minated the basement. When he reached the bottom of the stairs, he noticed that the professor had walked over to a wooden table and was picking up a small jar. He turned around and Max could see that the jar was an old canning jar that had holes punched in the lid. The jar was almost half-filled with dark, rich dirt.

"Here's what I wanted to show you," the professor said, holding out the jar for Max to see but not touch.

"That's amazing," Max joked.

The professor laughed. He unscrewed the top and tilted the

jar sideways to make the dirt shift toward the front. He slid in two fingers and began to sift through the dirt until he found what he was looking for. He gently pulled out a small worm about three inches long. It was a common brown worm that began to wiggle in the professor's grasp. He held the worm out for Max to see. "I call him Albert."

"Hello Albert," Max said, still unsure of what was going on and starting to feel a little foolish. But the professor's next words hit home and made Max automatically understand as well as frighten him.

"As far as I know," the professor said, "Albert here is the first time-traveler."

20

Unbelievable, Max thought as he stared in amazement at the professor's setup, which almost mimicked his own and also rested upon a thick iron plate on top of the floor of the basement. The microwave emitter seemed to be identical. The beta emitter was the same shape, but had a different color casing. The main difference, however, was the lead object. Instead of a ball, the professor had a box about three inches high, two inches wide, and two inches deep. Instead of one metal rod running through the lead, there were four, one on each corner, but still wrapped with heavy-duty, plastic coated wire. On top of the lead box was a circle about one inch in diameter which had a small slit, making it resemble the top of a flat-head screw.

"Does that open?" asked Max.

The professor answered his question by taking a flat head screwdriver and placing it in the slot on top of the box and turning counter-clockwise. The circle began to rise away from the top of the box until it unscrewed out completely.

"And that's where Albert rode?"

The professor nodded.

"Why a worm?" asked Max.

"I needed something alive that was small enough to fit in there," the professor replied. "Plus it made sense to send a worm through a wormhole."

Max smiled real big and nodded. Apparently it made sense to him also.

"Ready for a demonstration?" asked the professor.

"Yes," Max said without ever taking his eyes off the box.

The professor took Albert and lowered him into the box and then screwed the lid back on. He walked over to his control panel and signaled Max to join him.

"You don't use an amplifier?" Max asked as he walked over.

The professor shook his head. "I figure let's go out as far as it will go. Once we start perfecting it, we can try to figure out how to control the length of time it travels." He threw the switch and the box disappeared.

Max forgot how exciting it was to watch that happen. "Have you figured out if it's going forward or back?"

"No," the professor replied. "But I think it has to be going forward."

"Why is that?"

Professor Nowak shrugged his shoulders. "It just makes sense. If man were able to go back in time, we would have heard of this already."

Max considered the logic of that. It made sense, but wasn't an accurate barometer.

"What's the longest you've let it continue?" asked Max.

"I've left it for an hour with Albert inside. I wasn't sure how long a worm could go without air. Without Albert, I've let it stay a week."

Max looked up in amazement. Then he asked, "When did you build this?"

The professor gritted his teeth as if he was afraid to answer. "I ordered the emitters the night I left your house and started building the box that very weekend. It seemed like the next logical step in the experiment, to be able to test it on living things. I just never in a million years expected you to drop that bomb on me about ending it and throwing everything away. I hope you're not sore at me."

Max shook his head. "I'm glad you did. What else have you learned?"

"One thing," the professor noted, "is that if I leave the lid off, Albert does not go anywhere, but stays here with the rest of the non-lead items. But as long as the box is sealed, anything inside will travel with the box. I've sent grapes, water, metal objects, cloth, coins, and Albert. Nothing seems to be affected.

"Can I ask you a question?" the professor asked.

Max looked up and nodded.

"What made you change your mind?"

Max smiled. "My dad."

The professor was taken aback. "You told him?"

"No, of course not," Max said. "We just had a discussion about technology, and he pointed out that technology and inventions that can help mankind are good things, and that just because someone uses something to do harm, it doesn't make the machine evil."

The professor was surprised, but appreciative. He flipped the switch and the box instantly reappeared. He opened the top and took a self-made metal hook and reached in and pulled out Albert. He handed him to Max, who held his cupped hands up to his face to watch Albert wiggle around.

"Well," said Max "tell us what you saw. What did the worm girls of the future look like?"

The professor laughed. He was glad to finally tell Max and glad he was back on board, at least in spirit. But he didn't think it was quite time to tell Max everything.

Suddenly, an odd sequence of beeps filled the basement.

"What is that?" the professor asked while trying to locate the source.

Max pulled his cell phone out of his pocket and said, "Text." He read the message and said, "Uh oh."

"What is it?"

Max held up the phone so the professor could read the text from Julie: *To be good at math, you can't count minutes very well.*

They left the basement and the professor drove Max back to the campus.

***

It was a beautiful spring day, as about a hundred students had gathered around the tennis courts where Professor Nowak had decided to hold the results of the Near Impossible Assignment. The net had been taken down and a table had been set up midcourt.

Max stood with Julie by his side toward the front of the circle that the crowd had formed. He could see Rollo at the front of the circle across from him who would periodically give him a thumbs-up. Looking at the lineup, Max couldn't believe he was last. All the students competing, all eight of them, were listed alphabetically, and there was not one student with a last name after the letter M. Max wondered if the others competing were doing so out of a desire to succeed at the assignment like him, or at least his reason in the beginning, or if they were here desperately trying to improve their GPA, which was his reason now.

The professor stepped up to the table and everyone began to cheer. You could tell that he really enjoyed the popularity of this event. "OK," he said, motioning for everyone to lower their enthusiasm. "OK. Let's get started. But first I want to bring out my co-judge for this event."

Everyone including Max looked confused as someone made their way through the crowd to the table. Max smiled a little smile of disbelief as Brad Clavin walked up to join the professor amidst claps, cheers, and some jeers.

The very first student placed his ball upon the table when called upon; the professor took the magnet and approached the ball. When he got within an inch of the ball, it leaped up and stuck hard to the magnet. The student threw up his hands and the crowd went wild.

Max couldn't believe it.

Neither could the professor as he looked suspiciously at the joining. He pulled the ball away and looked it over. Then, he took a pocket knife and began to shave away the lead. Only about an eighth of an inch below the lead, the look of the metal changed to a bright, reflective tone.

"You covered a steel ball in lead?" the professor asked in disbelief.

The student put on his best innocent look as the crowd went from cheers to laughing.

The professor continued. "You have insulted the dignity of this event by attempting to cheat. I think that should call for negative points. But Brad, I leave this one up to you."

Brad played along as he pretended to flip through an imaginary rule book. "That's what it says in the rules."

The student wrapped his hands around his throat to show he had done himself in.

"But wait!" Brad announced, still looking in the invisible book. "There's an asterisk. If the dignity insulting is done with complete reckless abandon and a hint of style, it deserves no less than 15 bonus points."

"So let it be," the professor agreed to the cheers of the crowd as the student celebrated once more.

The day continued in the same fun manner. As the other students placed their ball on the table with their results, the professor would ask them what they made, and one by one Brad would determine their worth.

When Max was called, he felt a little self conscious about the joke he had planned since Brad was there but decided to go forward anyway. When the professor asked him for his ball, he pulled an object out of his pocket that he had borrowed from a member of his dad's congregation. Half of the crowd began laughing right away. Rollo was laughing so hard he was bent over slapping both legs.

"I had my lead ball made into this bullet," Max said raising it up high so everyone could see.

The professor laughed out loud and he turned and looked at Brad just as most everyone else had. Brad was just shaking his head with a wry smile on his face.

"So, Professor Nowak," Max continued, "if you will hold the magnet between your fingers, we will fire this bullet and you will see how attracted it becomes to the magnet."

The laughter continued.

"OK, I'm kidding." Max put the bullet back into his pocket, walked over to a cardboard box and opened it. Inside was a cordless drill for which he had locked the trigger to the "on" position and was still turning, albeit slowly. The battery was obviously drained. A small drill bit extended out of the drill and had been drilled into the lead ball. Two large magnets that Max had taken out of two old speakers were brushed up against the lead ball. It was the only thing Max could think to try at short notice, even though he even thought it was a silly idea to assume magnetism could be rubbed off.

The professor took the ball after Max had removed it from the drill bit and placed it on the table. As he scanned the magnet over it, Max thought he saw it move.

Am I seeing things? he wondered.

"It moved!" shouted Brad. "I saw it move."

The professor hadn't seen it since the magnet obscured his vision, but Rollo and others joined in proclaiming they had witnessed it also.

The crowd reacted with cheers and claps.

The professor calmed them down once again. "It seems like we have a winner. Max's ball was not picked up by the magnet, but his was the only one that reacted, at least legitimately. So for that he is awarded 50 bonus points."

As the crowd reacted again, Max breathed a sigh of relief. He knew he really needed those bonus points.

"Raise your hands," Julie instructed.

Max was about to hold his hands up in victory when he saw Brad whispering to the professor.

"Hold up, everyone," the professor cried out as the accolades died down. "Hold up. We have a secondary ruling from the other judge."

Max smiled at Julie as if to say it was too good to be true.

"My co-judge has suggested, and rightfully so, that the very sarcastic joke with the lead bullet be taken into account as well." The professor looked over at Max to see his reaction before continuing. "It is the ruling of my co-judge that said action was ruthless, vile, and unwarranted and, therefore, deserves an additional 20 bonus points."

The crowd erupted. Max lowered his head as he breathed a sigh of relief. He looked over at Brad.

Brad was smiling and shaking his finger at him as if explaining that Max had really gotten him on that bullet joke.

Max raised his hands in victory.

21

"That's very disheartening," Trish said as if she would begin to cry.

Max felt horrible. Sometimes he wished he wouldn't speak up during Bible study.

"Go on, Max," said the professor. "What other verses do you have to back up your views?"

Max didn't really pay attention to the professor's words, as he was still focusing on Trish. "I don't have all the answers. I could be wrong on everything."

Trish smiled at his attempt to console her. "Don't worry about me, Max. You have a right to your views and I appreciate them. It's just always been a comfort to think that when a loved one dies, they go to Heaven. But I know that not everyone believes that."

"I believe it," said Jenny as even she felt guilty having been the one to propose the topic. "I still believe it. I only chose to discuss that because Max always seems to use the phrase 'eternal life' instead of saying 'Heaven.'"

Kenneth agreed. "I noticed that, too."

The professor concurred. "I think we've all noticed that."

"Can we just move on to the next topic?" Max pleaded.

The professor looked at Trish.

"Oh no," she said. "No, you go ahead. I'm sorry. I didn't mean to make you uncomfortable. Please continue."

"Uh. . ." Max struggled to regain his train of thought. "John

3:13-15."

Rollo read, "No one has ever gone into heaven except the one who came from heaven — the Son of Man. Just as Moses lifted up the snake in the wilderness, so the Son of Man must be lifted up, that everyone who believes may have eternal life in him."

"Isaiah 60:21."

Jenny read, "Then all your people will be righteous and they will possess the land forever. They are the shoot I have planted, the work of my hands, for the display of my splendor."

"Psalm 37:11."

"But the meek shall inherit the earth; and shall delight themselves in the abundance of peace."

Max looked around the room. "And the Bible says that the earth will be made new again. So why else would it be made new if it wasn't going to be utilized?"

"Where is that at, Max?" Kenneth asked.

"About the earth being made new?"

Kenneth nodded.

"2 Peter 3:13."

   was Julie this time. "But in keeping with his promise, we are looking forward to a new Heaven and new earth, where righteousness dwells."

"Revelation 21:1."

   she read this time, which made Max feel better that she was composed enough to read "Then, I saw 'a new heaven and a new earth,' for the first heaven and the first earth had passed away, and there was no longer any sea."

"I don't think it should be a sad thing," Max offered, still trying to comfort her. "The gift of salvation will be the greatest thing in the entire universe no matter how God has it planned for us."

Trish smiled and nodded along with everyone else.

After a moment of silence, the professor realized it was over and looked at his notes for the next subject. "Oh, the last topic today is mine. It's really not mine, but I thought it would make a great topic since we touched upon it before. The topic is: 'Do the Elect make up everyone saved or only a specific group?'"

The sound of papers rustling could be heard as everyone got their notes ready.

The professor continued. "I emailed Brad and asked him to give us his point of view so we would have a starting point. Here's what he wrote back.

> "'The Elect' is a term used to describe everyone who will be saved because those were the ones chosen before the beginning of time to be saved. Nothing can change that. Scripture that proves this would be 1 Thessalonians 1:4 of the King James Bible."

The professor stopped there and looked around for someone to read, but no one had brought a King James Bible. He looked over at Jenny, but she held up her Bible to show that she had found her NIV. "Does anyone have a King James?" he asked.

"I have one in the car," Kenneth said.

The professor nodded so Kenneth hopped up and jetted out the door.

"While we wait on Kenneth," the professor said, "who agrees with Brad that the Elect make up everyone saved?"

Two guys raised their hands.

The professor motioned to one of them who said, "I don't have a specific scripture to prove it, but the way my pastor has always explained it is that since God is all-knowing, that means that He must know who will be saved. And since He created everything, it would have to have been determined from the beginning."

The professor nodded to the second guy who only offered the same explanation.

"That's the way I've always heard it too. Since God knows everything, then it must be set in stone."

Several people started to respond at once, but the professor stopped them.

Kenneth came back in a little out of breath, but holding the King James Bible. He took his seat and waited for his cue.

"Let's get back on track here. Kenneth, can you read Brad's verse?"

"Sure. What was it again?"

The professor looked at his notes. "1 Thessalonians 1:4."

Kenneth read, "Knowing, brethren beloved, your election of God."

"And 1 Corinthians 6:2," continued the professor.

"Still from the King James?" asked Kenneth.

"Sure, go ahead," the professor replied.

"Do ye not know that the saints shall judge the world? And if the world shall be judged by you, are ye unworthy to judge the smallest matters?"

"OK," the professor summarized. "Brad says that this proves that the Elect does describe everyone who will be saved. Now who wants to go first?"

Several people raised their hands. Rollo was called on first.

"I just want to address the point this guy made," he said motioning in the direction of the two who had agreed with Brad. "I agree that God is all-knowing but that doesn't mean he didn't give us free will. If you give a five-year-old two choices, present for his birthday, lay and one else say pony and one is a box of broken glass, do we know which one he will choose."

Everyone nodded.

Rollo continued. "But knowing which one he will choose did not take away his free will."

Max smiled.

Rollo noticed his friend's expression. "What? You thought I was just another pretty face?"

Everyone laughed.

"Yeah," Max said. "That's exactly what I thought."

Several others spoke up with similar sentiment. Finally, the professor called on Max.

"To be honest," Max began, "I never even knew there were people who thought that. When Paul sends letters to the church in Corinth, or the church in Thessalonica, or the church in Ephesus, it's not hard to imagine that those members, or at least some of them, would indeed be part of those chosen. After all, they were preaching the gospel of Jesus at a time when it was outlawed and the consequences were dire. People were beheaded for that back then. And that coincides with Revelation 20:4."

The group was listening closely so the sudden verse caught them off-guard. Only a few flipped to find it. One read, "I saw thrones on which were seated those who had been given authority to judge. And I saw the souls of those who had been beheaded because of their testimony about Jesus and because of the word of God. They had not worshiped the beast or its image and had not received its mark on their foreheads or their hands. They came to life and reigned with Christ a thousand years."

Max continued. "And the points Rollo and these others made about free will is a great point. I think it's obvious that we all have free will or why else would we be instructed to try to save as many people as we can? If it had all been decided long ago and nothing could change it, what power could our words have? For that matter, why did Jesus and Paul spend so much time trying to save as many people as they could? Look at what lengths they went to. 1 Corinthians 9:19-23."

Kenneth, who had gone back to the NIV, read, "Though I am free and belong to no one, I have made myself a slave to everyone, to win as many as possible. To the Jews I became like a Jew, to win the Jews. To those under the law, I became like one under the law (though I myself am not under the law), so as to win those under the law. To those not having the law I became like one not having the law (though I am not free from God's law, but am under Christ's law), so as to win those not having the law. To the weak I became weak, to win the weak. I have become all things to all people so that by all possible means I might save some. I do all this for the sake of the gospel, that I may share in its blessings.'"

As had become the norm, heads began to nod around the circle.

"Matthew 9:10-12," added Max.

Jenny read, "While Jesus was having dinner at Matthew's house, many tax collectors and sinners came and ate with him and his disciples. When the Pharisees saw this, they asked his disciples, 'Why does your teacher eat with tax collectors and sinners?' On hearing this, Jesus said, 'It is not the healthy who need a doctor, but the sick.'"

"Why wasn't he sitting with the Elect?" asked Trish.

"Exactly," Max said, nodding to her. "For that matter, if the Elect makes up everyone and was decided long ago, why did Jesus even have to come to earth? None of it makes sense."

"Interesting," the professor said amongst the nods.

"And one more thing," Max continued. "There is something else that really doesn't seem right about the idea of it all being predetermined. First, why would there even be a judgment day or why would anyone need to be judged at all if God decided it long ago? That would be like picking out Miss Alabama to be the next Miss America before the contest began and having everyone it's been decided but they're going to go through the motions anyway or the heck of it."

Snickers and giggles filled the room.

Max laughed at himself. "I couldn't think of a good metaphor."

"No. That was good," said the professor.

Everyone agreed.

"And when Paul mentions the 'saints' in 1 Corinthians and Revelation mentions them in chapter 20, it says they will be judging on judgment day. So who are they judging if it has already been decided that they are the winners and everyone else are the losers? If Brad's theory is correct and they are the only ones saved, then every single person they are judging is going to be cast into the lake of fire. So why does it need to be done at all? But the

Bible doesn't say that. The last line of Revelation 20 says anyone whose name was not found written in the book of life was thrown into the lake of fire. That would indicate to me that some names were found written in the book of life, hopefully a lot of names."

Everyone sat there as Max's words sank in.

"OK," said the professor. "How many think that the Elect make up only the group of pre-chosen ones that will be judging the rest of us, good or bad, on judgment day and that that term does not refer to everyone who will be saved?"

Everyone in the room, including the professor, and the two who had originally raised their hands to agree with Brad, raised their hands.

"Whoa, whoa," said the professor as everyone began to lower their hands. He reached inside his pants pocket and pulled out his cell phone. He held it up and scanned it around as to find the best angle to snap a picture. "Raise your hands again. I need to send Brad an email and let him know the outcome."

Everyone laughed and looked around at each other as if they had never seen Professor Nowak's devious side.

22

It was an early Tuesday morning, and Max came downstairs and headed toward the front door. He didn't even stop to grab a bite for breakfast. Before he reached the front door, however, he was surprised to hear his dad calling from the kitchen. He turned to walk back and noticed his dad still in his pajamas, unshaven, sitting at the kitchen table.

"What's up, Dad? I'm in a hurry."

"That's what's up," his dad replied and motioned for him to take a seat. As Max sat down across from him, he continued. "You're always in a hurry and I would like a few minutes to talk to you. Is that okay?"

"I'm sorry," Max said, a little embarrassed of himself. "Of course that's okay."

His father tried to start on a positive note. "We're really proud of you. You finished your second semester with an A. Again. But since Julie is at home during the summer working, we thought you would be working full-time at Hurley's again this summer. We were just a little surprised that you stayed part-time and are spending so much time with Professor Nowak."

Max listened, but wasn't sure what to say. There wasn't a question in there anywhere.

Sensing that, his father was more direct. "What are you doing with the professor over summer break?"

"I'm helping him with a project."

"That's the thing," his dad clarified. "Why all the secrecy?

This isn't like you."

Max realized he was right; it wasn't like him. "The professor asked me to not say anything to anyone until it was ready. I gave him my word."

His dad nodded his understanding. He wouldn't want Max to break his word. "It's not illegal, right?"

Max laughed. "No, dad, not illegal. But we think it's going to be huge."

"One last question," his dad said. "Of all the students he has, why did he pick you to help?"

"He didn't," Max answered. "It was my discovery. I just didn't want the recognition so I allowed the professor to take over. I'm just helping him out. That's all."

His dad couldn't help but smile. As Max went out the front door, he felt a little better after the talk, but still couldn't shake the feeling of worry.

***

Max sat on a folding chair in the professor's basement, thumbing through a stack of papers. "I can't believe you have been continuing these experiments for the last two months. These are very good notes."

"I didn't want to put them on the computer," said the professor. "I am too afraid of hackers."

"Good point," agreed Max as he continued to read over the professor's notes complete with a diagram of how to build the time unit along with everything he had tried so far. "Looking at your notes here, I'm not sure what else you can do with this box."

The professor smiled.

Max recognized that smile. "You've already started on the next step, haven't you?"

"Let's go for a ride," the professor said.

It was still early on a beautiful summer day as they took the professor's truck and headed north along several rural roads. The sun was still low enough in the sky that it almost appeared like a strobe light as the trees adorning the road with almost perfect spacing allowed the light of the sun to blink in and out as they rode.

"So where are we heading?"

The professor took the index finger of his right hand and pointed it forward without letting go of the steering wheel. "The house where I grew up. My mom and dad left it to me."

They made small talk along the way, and Professor Nowak told Max that he had attended Cedarbluff and got a job teaching high school after he graduated. But when the job came open at the university, he put in for it, but really didn't think he had a chance. But he got the call and had been teaching there ever since.

Max noticed a sign on the right side of the road that read, *Welcome to Michigan*. He didn't say anything because he trusted the professor. About 50 minutes after the trip began, they pulled into an old homestead.

The house had old wooden siding that hadn't seen a paint brush for many years. There were some broken panes of glass, and the roof was actually concave and one had to wonder just how much longer the after could hold out. There was once a gravel driveway but that had been overrun with grass and weeds. Max could tell that the professor and maybe others had been there recently from the tire tracks through the grass, some even went around to the back of the house.

The professor grabbed a flashlight out of the console of his truck. "We're here," he said as he walked toward the front door.

Max followed him inside. It was musty and dark. The professor had him wait while he went down into the basement. Max looked around in disbelief. He couldn't understand why the professor would choose this place over his house near the campus.

A whining noise was heard like an engine's pistons straining against the cylinder housing of an internal combustion engine. This was followed by a few sputters and then a steady hum at which point the basement was illuminated by bright, fluorescent light.

"Come on down," the professor shouted.

Max was filled with curiosity and even a little fear as he descended the steps, each wooden plank making its own distinct creak as he eased down into the unknown. When he reached the bottom step, before even touching the basement floor, he stared in wonderment.

"You've been busy, Dr. Frankenstein."

The professor smiled.

Max's eyes scanned the room. The really large generator was humming along in the corner. There was a very large white plastic tank within a few feet that housed the gasoline. The exhaust pipe was run through a hole in one of the basement windows, which consisted of glass blocks. It looked as if the hole was already there and perhaps was the exhaust outlet for a washer and dryer at one time. Wires also ran to a box that sat beside ten car batteries. Max assumed it was a charger to keep the batteries from going dead. He could tell all the light fixtures were brand new, as the contrast between them and the musky basement was obvious. There were two new laptop computers sitting on a new conference table. There were two bulletin boards and one chalkboard. It looked more like the security guard room of an institution for the criminally insane than it did a laboratory. But it was clear that one thing was missing.

"Where's the box?" asked Max.

The professor smiled. "Come with me."

He led Max back up the steps into the main part of the house and went out the back door. The back yard had been mowed recently, and there was a large grouping of wires that led from the house to an area about ten square feet where the grass was missing and the dirt was fresh. Halfway down one side of this square area was another smaller square area jutting off about three square feet. It was just a hole. The professor headed for that very spot.

Max looked down in the hole and couldn't believe what he saw. About three feet down was a trap-door configuration of sorts.

The material of the door was almost transparent, and he could tell that beneath the door was empty space, mainly because the area was illuminated. Max assumed that the lights were rigged to come on with the generator.

The professor grabbed a rope attached to the door and pulled it until the lock released and the door opened downward. Then, just like the basement of the house, he headed down without so much as an invitation for Max to follow. That part was understood.

Max followed the professor's motions by sitting on the edge of the hole and placing his foot on the first step, and then slowly descended down into this underground hideout. When he reached the bottom, he gasped. The basement in the house was nothing compared to what he was now seeing.

The walls were concrete blocks, but the ceiling was the same transparent material as the door. It had two long fluorescent lights mounted on it. There were video cameras mounted in the upper corners of one wall. Right in the middle of the room was a six-foot-tall lead box. On either side of the box were giant emit-ers that were also mounted to each wall no doubt near that one was for microwaves and one for beta rays. Large metal rods protruded from the top and bottom corners of the box and were wrapped with coated wire about one half-inch in diameter. A the wiring went through the roof. But the thing that caught Max's eye the most was the oval outline on one side of the box that had large hinges on one side and a round metal steering-wheel looking object in the middle. It resembled a door you might see on a submarine.

The professor began his tour. "The walls are made from solid concrete blocks which are two feet deep. The ceiling is made from one-foot-thick Plexiglass. I've basically calculated the specs of the smaller unit at my house and magnified everything evenly. There's no reason it shouldn't work."

"Wow." Max was totally stunned. "When I said the next step, I was thinking we would build one about a foot tall. This is too much. How much did all this cost you?"

"Almost all I had saved."

Max stared up at the professor in disbelief.

"This is the next step, Max," the professor argued. "I figured it would be safer underground so it isn't visible to anyone. We're three feet beneath the surface so if this area is covered with concrete in the future, hopefully it will still be above this room. I can drill a hole right through the Plexiglass door, through the soil, and know right away if there's concrete above or not. Let me show you."

"How would you fill the area with dirt above the door?" asked Max. "I mean, if no one was staying behind?"

"It should fill in automatically after a few rainy days," said the professor.

He turned the wheel on the door counterclockwise and opened it. Inside was a seating section big enough for two.

"That's why I went with a generator," the professor continued. I didn't want to take a chance of a tree falling on a power line or a breaker flipping off. If you'll notice on the back wall, I've installed an on/off switch to the power so it can be controlled from within the box. This will give us a constant flow of power, ensuring that the box remains with us in the future until we get ready to come back, which we can control as well."

"No, no, no," said Max holding up both hands and shaking them along with his head. "Not 'we.'"

"What do you mean?" asked the professor. "This is your invention."

"Yes, but I don't have any desire to be the one to try it out." Max looked up from the box and directly at the professor. "I think we need people like astronauts or something."

"Have you ever heard of the Wright Brothers?" asked the professor.

Max didn't answer, nor did he need to.

The professor continued to plead his case. "Did they have someone try out their invention first? No! They did it themselves."

Max stood firm. "If you want to do it, I understand. But I don't. I'll help out any way I can. It will probably be best to have someone stay here to monitor everything anyway."

The professor conceded.

Changing the subject, Max asked, "How many times have you tested it?"

The professor finally lightened his demeanor and smiled. "Zero. I've been waiting on you."

Max was glad.

"It's ready for its first test today if you're ready," said the professor.

Max smiled. "Let's do it."

They walked back inside and down into the basement again. The professor turned the computers on, typed some keys on the keyboard, and the monitors displayed the inside of the underground room.

Max recognized the angles as being from the two cameras he had seen in the corners mounted to the concrete walls.

The professor looked at Max and asked, "What do you think?"

Max pond̶e̶r̶e̶d̶ ... ̶c̶ ... ̶a̶ ̶s̶ ̶o̶n̶e̶ ̶"̶ ̶1̶ ̶b̶ ̶g̶ concern is how much ... ̶i̶n̶g̶ ... ̶i̶c̶ ̶c̶ ̶i̶c̶ ̶t̶ is obviously bigger th̶a̶n̶ ... ̶a̶n̶d̶ ̶h̶ ̶a̶ ̶c̶ ̶a̶ ̶o̶ house."

The profes̶s̶o̶r̶ ... ̶e̶r̶. ̶E̶ ̶t̶ ̶h̶ ̶r̶ ̶h̶ ̶o̶ way t̶o̶ find out." He p̶ ̶d̶ ... ̶o̶t̶ ̶v̶ ̶t̶ ̶n̶ ̶d̶ the wall of the basement and waited for Max to give the go-ahead.

Max gave him a thumbs-up and the professor flipped the switch. Max watched his laptop monitor closely and saw the large lead box disappear. It worked. He knew there was no reason for it not to, but still couldn't believe it had.

But the professor's monitor went blank.

After turning the switch back to the off position, they ventured out to the underground room. Everything seemed fine except one camera was completely missing along with small chunks of concrete where the bolts had pulled out of the wall.

Max and the professor walked over and looked at the area where the camera had been mounted. The professor looked around the room and around the time unit to see if he could find it.

"I think it's gone," said Max. "Just like your pen."

The professor laughed. "The people in the future are getting all my best stuff."

Max ran his fingers around the hole in the concrete wall. "I guess that answers the question about suction."

❧23❧

Max sat back against his headboard with his knees pulled up almost against him. "I miss you, too," he whispered into the cordless phone.

"I'm not so sure," said Julie on the other end. "We hardly ever talk anymore because you spend so much time with Professor Nowak. I think he is more important than me."

This was a new phase in their relationship and yet another situation that Max wasn't equipped to handle. He knew that he had been spending more time on the experiment and less time talking to Julie, but his feelings hadn't changed, yet he could not find the words to convince h

"What do you w   re to   he asked

"That's just   ra lie   I have to e y   s coun "

Max was   r   ra

"Did I ev r   ur   d Fifth St e
she asked.

Max searched his memory. "I don't think so."

Julie explained. "It's this beautiful old church that has been here forever. It closed down before I was born, but it's always been a landmark here. You remind me of that old church, and every time I see the church, I think of you."

Max smiled. It was an odd comparison, but a nice one.

"I drove by there yesterday," Julie continued, with her voice breaking up, "and the whole area was roped off and the church was being demolished."

Max could hear her crying, but he didn't understand why. "I'm sorry; I'm not following."

Julie tried to stop crying. "That's what I feel is happening to our relationship."

"They were probably tearing it down because it was dangerous, Julie."

"I realize that," she snapped. "But I think it was a sign."

Max had gotten used to Julie's signs, which seem to manifest themselves to her at the drop of a hat.

"Look," he comforted. "I miss you. I miss you so much. I miss us spending every day together. I can't wait until the fall semester so we can spend every day together again. But this thing with the professor is huge like The Wright Brothers huge. I would rather be spending time with you or even talking with you on the phone, but I feel obligated to continue this experiment all the way out."

This made her feel better.

***

Max sat at the table in front of the computers reading over the professor's notes, which now included details of experiments done on the full-cale model. "OK, we've run tests with water and other materials. We've run tests while videoing oxygen sensors, Geiger counters, and thermometers. Everything has come up great – perfect temperature, perfect oxygen, and no radiation. So what should we try next?"

"I think we're ready for a live subject. Maybe we should go to a pet store and get a guinea pig or something." The professor looked at Max for his thoughts.

Max shook his head. "I don't know if we're ready for that. First of all, we don't even know if this thing is going forward in time or not. I think that should be the first thing to determine. Then, we need to see if your underground cell remains intact. For all we know, it's not even there anymore or perhaps the roof has caved in."

The professor concurred. "That's a very good point. But how do we determine these things?"

Both he and Max studied that question. The professor began to pace around the room with his hands behind his back like you might imagine an expectant father doing in a hospital waiting room. Max took a legal pad and began to sketch.

Several minutes went by and Max called out, "How about this?"

The professor walked over to look at Max's crude rendering.

Seeing his confused look, Max explained. "OK, we know that if the box is sealed, everything inside will transfer. Correct? Alright, but do we know if that seal has to be made of lead?"

The professor began to get the picture. He could tell Max had drawn the door on the lead box and had added a circle above the hatch lock. "A window?"

"If it works, we could set up a video camera and see outside the box," Max suggested.

The professor had his doubts. "I don't think the window will travel."

"It wouldn't necessarily have to," Max countered. "As long as it kept the seal while the box is here, it should let everything inside transfer. What do you think?"

The professor rolled out his bottom lip as he was thinking. "It's worth a try."

***

Two weeks later and they were ready to go again. The professor had contacted the company where he had purchased the Plexiglass and had them make him a piece out of the one-foot-thick material that was only six inches wide by three inches high. Although lead is a soft metal, he and Max realized it was a tough job cutting a specific size hole in the lead door since it and the walls of the box were also a foot thick. But they got it done and got the little window installed and sealed off.

First, they tried it with no camera to see what would happen. When the switch was thrown, the box disappeared. Max and the professor stared at both monitors since both were operational, having replaced the camera that disappeared. They both noticed it at the same time. The Plexiglass window was there as if levitating in mid-air.

The professor turned it off and the box reappeared with the window back in its place. He looked at Max and said, "Let's go mount a camera."

Unlike the cameras mounted inside the room, they used a camera that would record to a memory stick. They wouldn't be able to see the results until after they brought the box back. They mounted it to the door itself directly under the window. Adjusting it so the camera was flush up against the Plexiglass and pointing directly out the window, they set it to record and went back inside.

"We'll know right away," said the professor. "If we flip the switch and the box disappears, but we still see the camera, we'll know it didn't work."

He flipped the switch.

"YES!" Max yelled.

The professor looked closely at the monitor, which confirmed that the window was there but that the camera was not. He let it go for about 30 seconds before turning it off.

They walked out, retrieved the camera, and brought it back into the basement. The professor took the connector wire and hooked one end to the camera and one end to the computer. It showed there was one video in the memory. The professor clicked on it as the excitement grew. It was total blackness.

"Did it not work?" asked Max.

The professor leaned in to take a closer look and then started to laugh.

Max got tickled at the professor laughing and began to

laugh himself. "What is it?"

The professor shook his head and turned to look at Max. "I don't know if the room is there or not, but if it is, it would be dark."

Max nodded and wondered what kinds of scientists they were. Of course there would be no light in the room way into the future.

They went out to the unit again and mounted a nice flashlight beside the camera. Max turned the flashlight on and the professor started the recorder on the camera. They walked back into the house again and down into the basement. The professor flipped the switch and waited another 30 seconds. He cut the power and back out they went to retrieve the camera once again.

This time when they began the video, it was not black, but still not perfectly clear. They each stared at the monitor trying to make heads or tails of what they were seeing.

"I see it." Max said. "Do you see it?"

The professor didn't answer, but leaned in closer.

Max took his fingers and began to trace very faint lines on the screen. After he did this four times, the professor whispered, "Steps."

Max and the professor looked at each other and laughed. It was indeed steps, which meant the room was still there and intact.

"That's the best thing I've seen today since I saw a piece of Plexiglass levitating," the professor joked.

"Wait a minute," Max said.

"What?"

Max smiled at the professor. "This means that there is an opening the size of our window in the future. Right?"

The professor thought for a second. "Yeah, it does mean that."

"Well, don't you see?" asked Max. "That means we can now take measurement of the environment outside the box."

"Oh my gosh. You're right. Let's do it."

Max and the professor rounded up the thermometer, the oxygen sensor, and the Geiger counter and took them out to the unit. They sat them all in a row on one seat and activated them. Next, they mounted a camera in front of each one of them. They were the same kinds of cameras they had just used to view outside the window. Then, they went back inside and threw the switch again.

"I think we should leave them for a couple of hours to be sure we get good readings," said the professor.

Max agreed.

"Let's go grab some lunch then."

It was already 3 p.m., and Max just now realized he hadn't eaten all day so he agreed with the professor. They had to drive about 15 miles just to get to a McDonalds. They went in and ordered, then took a seat. There were no other customers in the restaurant.

As they began to eat, the professor said, "This will be an important test today."

Max nodded as he chewed his food.

The professor continued. "It's one thing to know that the air is safe inside the box, but we need to know if it's safe to open the door. It won't tell us what the surface environment is like, but it's still an important step.

"Have you ever read *The Time Machine*?" he asked, changing the subject.

Max nodded. "I have the complete collection of H.G. Wells."

"There's one thing about that book that I don't think the author took into account."

"What was that?" Max asked.

"In the book," said the professor, "the time traveler went over 800,000 years into the future. Remember?"

Max couldn't remember exactly, but he nodded so the professor would continue.

"Well, one reason we have a stable environment is because of the exact positioning of our moon. But the moon is receding from the earth at a rate of about an inch a year. So in 800,000 years, that's almost 70,000 feet. I don't think the environment would be a friendly place then. There would most likely be a more discernable wobble to the planet causing severe earthquakes, storms, and all kinds of natural disasters. That would be the norm. But in the book, he depicts a very peaceful climate. I just always thought that was a bad depiction."

Max shook his head. "That's depressing and a little scary. Are you sure you really want to go through with this?"

The professor laughed. He realized that it wasn't the best story to tell since he was still hoping to convince Max to join him. Maybe it was time for some damage repair. "I don't think our unit is going anywhere near that far into the future."

They finished their meal and drove back to the house. "Here goes," said the professor as he cut the power.

After retrieving the cameras, they hooked them up to the computers and played the videos. What they saw shocked them. The temperature was 70 degrees and the air in the underground room seemed to be cleaner in the future than it was now. The Geiger counter registered nothing. All signs seemed good to go.

24

Taking off the top, Max stuck his hand in the shoe box and gently rubbed the top of the hamster's head. It twisted his head to make Max's fingers hit the spots it wanted to get the most attention. Max smiled.

"What do you want to name him?" asked the professor.

"Nothing," said Max. "I don't want to give him a name until he gets back."

The professor understood. "Well, that's all we really need to do this morning. We got his food, water bowl, and plenty of newspapers. Let's send him on his way. Don't you have to work today?"

"It's gonna be okay," Max whispered to the hamster without addressing the professor's question. "You're gonna be fine."

They went out to the time unit, and the professor spread out the newspapers on the floor, then placed a large bowl of hamster food and a large bowl of water on top of the newspapers. They had the three cameras mounted to the ceiling. They had programmed one to start recording after two days, one to start after one day, and one they turned on right away after placing the hamster on the floor. They walked out and closed and locked the hatch.

Max walked to his truck and waited for the professor to go down and flip the switch and come back out. "I'll see you Friday at 8:00 a.m.," he said as the professor emerged from the house. He got into his truck and headed back to his mom and dad's to get ready for work.

His dad was on a plumbing job when he got home. He grabbed a sandwich and started to head back out when his mom came in from her garden.

"Hey, can I talk to you a minute?" she asked.

"I'm running late," Max replied.

She looked down at the floor, then back up at Max. "How about tonight when you get in?"

"Sure, Mom," he said as he gave her a kiss on the cheek and went out the door.

As he drove to work, he almost wished he had called in to say he was going to be late. It dawned on him that his mom had never asked him that before. It was he and his dad who had the talks, so for his mom to ask, it must have been important to her.

He tried to put it out of his mind as he started work. He tried to put everything out of his mind, but as the day progressed, his mom, Julie, and the little hamster would leave him no peace.

"We sure could have used you yesterday." Mr. Mitner had come up behind him as he was working in the warehouse.

"Sorry about that," Max replied.

Mr. [ ]ig[ ]rec[ ]a[ ]o g[ ]' [ ]m[ ]ly o[ ]ed[ ]since [ ]
bloc[ ]on h[ ] [ ]by t[ ] [ ]trip[ ]r d[ ]d g o [ ]he h[ ]
pita[ ]I cal[ ]r[ ]la[ ]he call[ ]n[ ]pa[ ]a s[ ]h[ ]got n
touc[ ]with[ ]it[ ]c u ln[ ]on[ ]n Yo[ ]u v[ ]ond ays; e
the[ ]we[ ]n t c[ ]ve [ ]s.'

"I w[ ]of[ ]vn'[ ]Ma[ ]ek l[ ]n[ ]

Mr. [ ]k[ ]v l[ ]va[ ]' t n[ ]f[ ]ou b[ ]ow an l co d have come in if he had wanted to. Like everyone else that had contact with Max, he could tell he had changed. He turned to walk away.

Max could feel it, too. It made him feel bad considering that Mr. Mitner had begun to treat him differently after he graduated, as a peer even instead of an employee. That was gone now. Not only did Mr. Mitner see him as only an employee again, but an unreliable one. Between his parents and Julie and now Mr. Mitner, he longed for the experiment to be over so things could get back to normal. When the professor first told him that he hoped they could be ready for a human test before the fall semester began, Max tried to tell him that they shouldn't rush. But now he thought the professor was right.

Max got off at eleven o'clock that night and drove home. As he walked into the house, he didn't even turn any lights on as he started up the stairs. Then, he noticed that the light above the stove in the kitchen was on and he went back down to turn it off. He knew that was odd because his mom didn't usually leave something like that on.

When he walked into the kitchen, his mom was getting up from her chair.

"Oh, Mom, I'm sorry. Please don't get up. I just forgot."

"No, honey," his mom said. "You're probably tired."

"No, I'm fine. I just forgot, that's all." Max sat down at the table and motioned for his mom to sit back down.

"OK. But let me get you something to eat. I saved some supper." She reached into the microwave and pulled out a paper plate with a paper towel draped over it and set it in front of him before taking her seat.

Max removed the paper towel to reveal a plate of spaghetti and a hard roll. He didn't realize how hungry he was until he saw that. He began to eat as his mom collected her thoughts.

"I just wanted to talk about Julie," she began.

Max stopped eating and looked up at her.

"It's your life," his mom continued, "but she cares about you so much, and I know how worried she is that you guys are drifting apart."

"How do you know that?" Max asked.

"We talk on the phone sometimes."

"I know she's worried, Mom. I don't have a lot of experience in these matters, so I don't know how to word it to make her feel better. But I love her, Mom. I know that much. I can't imagine ever loving anyone like I love her. But I have to finish what I started here so she and I can go back to the way we were come the fall semester."

His mom had a huge smile on her face.

"What?" Max didn't know why she was smiling.

"Have you told Julie these things?"

Max looked down at his plate. "She knows."

His mom reached over and patted his hand. "Knowing something and hearing it are two different things." She got up to go to bed. "It sounds to me like you do know the right things to say; you just haven't said them yet."

As she closed her bedroom door behind her, Max knew she was right. He had wanted to tell Julie many times, but was so afraid. He kept hoping she would be the first to say it, but he knew that was cowardly to expect her to take the lead all the time in their relationship. He looked at the clock on the wall. It was almost midnight. He took his cell phone and dialed.

"Hello?" came the groggy answer on the other end after the third ring.

"Hey, it's Max."

"I know," Julie said. "My other boyfriends never call this late. I everythin w n ?"

, no ca r. I've j st been thinking about you all day nd wa d to al.

e sin l. W l, I gue s I can forgive you ther."

ante d el yo hat I just realized somethin about myself Ma it, l Jul di dn't respond so he contin ed. "I realize hat a w d m.'

"You just now realized that?" Julie laughed. "That's usually the first thing people notice about you."

Max laughed, too. He was glad she had lightened the mood. "I love your sense of humor."

"Why thank you."

Max swallowed hard. "It's not just your sense of humor. It's everything about you. I've been trying to say these things to you for a long time, but I've been too chicken. I'm sorry for that. But Julie. . . I love you."

Silence.

Had she hung up? "Julie, are you there?"

Silence.

Max checked his phone to make sure it still had power and was still showing connected. It was.

"Julie?"

Then, he could hear it – soft, gentle sobs. It was such a contrast to her crying before. "Are you okay?" he asked.

"Yes. I'm more than okay," she was finally able to say. "I love you, too."

***

Max's alarm went off at 6:00 a.m. He got up and tried to clear his eyes and mind. Today was the big day. He was not scheduled to work, and he wanted to get as early a start as possible. He went downstairs, took a shower, and came back up to get dressed. The sun was peeking through his curtains as he threw on his shoes. He walked over to his dresser and picked up a box of hamster food, lifted the door to the large plastic encasement, and filled the little bowl.

"There you go, Deuce."

Deuce, so named because he had become the second successful time traveler, came out of his sleeping compartment to eat.

Max went downstairs and out the door.

He was so excited as he drove the familiar route to Professor Nowak's family home in rural southern Michigan. The professor's truck was already there when he arrived.

He took his keys and opened the several new locks on the front door and walked down into the basement. The professor smiled when he saw him. He looked nervous.

"How do you feel?" Max asked.

"Truthfully, a little nervous. I couldn't sleep a wink last night."

Max understood. "We've got a lot of different tests to run

so let's get started."

The first thing on the list was to run a test sending every-thing the professor would eventually take with him. That con-sisted of a backpack filled with clothes, sleeping bag, medicine, bottled water, food, and a camera.

As Max ran through the contents to make sure everything was there, he noticed the odd goggles on the table. "Are those the spy vision things you were telling me about?"

The professor nodded.

"Can I try them?"

"Sure," the professor said. He took the goggles and handed them to Max. They almost looked like night-vision goggles except for the weird tentacle protruding out of the center of them and curling around about six feet long.

Max slipped them over his head and positioned them snug-gly over his eyes. "Now how do they work?"

The professor took the end of the tentacle and pointed it at his face. "Can you see me?"

Max laughed. "Yeah, it's like looking through the peep hole in a dorm room's front door."

"When I drill the hole in the Plexiglass door and hopefully all the way through the ground, I slide this fiber optic cord up through the hole. Once it's on the outside, I turn this knob."

Max held the goggles off so he could watch the professor turn a knob at the base of the cord, which rested right between the eye section of the goggles. As he turned it, the very end of the cord, the farthest part away from the goggles, began to bend. As he turned it more, the cord became a ninety-degree angle.

"This is how I will be able to turn it all around and see what's out there," the professor said.

Max thought that was so cool.

Besides the backpack and goggles, the professor would be taking along a heavy-duty, fully charged cordless drill and a shov-el to dig out through the dirt above the door, if indeed it was only dirt. They had accepted the fact that civilization probably covered this area in which case the professor would only try to look upon the future and not attempt to explore it.

They carried everything out to the time unit, and as they started putting everything inside, Max noticed something new. On the inside back wall was what appeared to be a small scuba unit.

"What is that?" asked Max a little bothered that the professor would be adding new stuff this late in the experiment.

"I began to worry about the quality of air above the ground," the professor explained. "Plus, for all we know, it could be underwater now. I thought it couldn't hurt to have emergency oxygen in case that was the difference in getting back inside the box or not."

"I never thought of that," Max admitted. "It makes sense, but we should have already tested it with this. But I guess we will be testing it with the equipment run."

"Exactly. I bought two of them by the way."

Max looked at Professor Nowak with a disappointed look. "You promised not to do that."

"I know," confessed the professor. "But I'm getting really scared. I know it will be safer with two people going."

Max sympathized with him, but he had made his decision. "You don't have to do it, you know."

The professor thought on that for a second, then said, "Yeah, I really do."

Every test had been successful and event-free. They had sent the
equipment through several times in pieces and several times all
together. It was already getting late in the afternoon.

"We gotta do this." The professor said.

Max was so nervous. How would he explain this if something went wrong?

The professor went over the instructions again. "Remember, the first time I want you to flip the switch from in here. Count
to five seconds and then turn it off."

Max

OK,

Max

so   ta   as h   c   t   t

cracks were   is

few se onds   s   r   t   u

The fir test

tools or backpack. He watched the professor enter the time unit
and turn the handle to secure it. Max's cell phone rang and he
answered it.

"OK. I'm in. Let's do it," the professor said.

Max flipped the switch. He did it quickly so he wouldn't
back out. He closed his eyes and counted off five seconds and
cut the power. He checked the monitors. The box was there. He
ran up the stairs to the door, opened it, and climbed down into the
room. He turned the handle and opened the door.

There sat the professor smiling.

"You did it," yelled Max.

The professor walked out of the time unit with a strange look on his face.

"How do you feel?'

"Who are you?" asked the professor.

"What?"

The professor started laughing.

"That's not funny," snapped Max.

"I'm sorry," said the professor. "You should have seen the look on your face. No, I feel perfectly normal."

Max wanted complete details. "Did you sense anything happening at all?"

"Let's go back inside so we can write it all down as I tell it," said the professor.

Max agreed. They went back inside, sat at the computer table, and Max grabbed the notebook to take notes.

"I could definitely tell when it happened because there was a sudden vibration. And I could hear a slight ringing that may or may not have been caused by the vibration. Maybe breaking the time barrier is like breaking the sound barrier." He looked at Max and smiled. "Did I just time-travel?"

Max laughed. "Yeah, you did. Do you feel like you have time lag or anything like that?"

The professor shook his head. "I don't feel anything except euphoria right now. We should have brought something to drink. I'm still shaking."

"No drinking while time traveling," Max joked. "Everybody knows that."

"Let's do the second step right now," the professor said. It was almost like he was high on a drug. "Let me go through with the drill and goggles and let's find out now if exploration is even a possibility."

"We're jumping a step," cited Max. "You need to go through and make sure the switch works on the inside of the unit."

"That's right," the professor acknowledged. "I'll go do that now. Don't touch the switch. I will count to five and come back. If I'm not back in ten seconds, flip the switch. It is set up like a two-way light switch, so if it's on in the box, then cutting it on in here cuts the power."

Max understood and watched the professor go out and get in the box. Three seconds later, it disappeared. Max crossed his fingers and held his breath. Five seconds later, it reappeared. Max exhaled.

The professor jumped out and came running back in like a kid. They sat and wrote notes for a while to make sure to document everything.

"Now for the drill and goggles," the professor said.

Max agreed and watched again as the professor left the basement and entered the time unit, this time with the drill and goggles. Max watched the monitors as the box disappeared again. Then he sat and waited and watched the clock.

He tried to imagine how long it would take for the professor to drill through — that is, providing he was able to. The wait was unbear_____ to what had happened.

The professor walked down to the basement with Max close behind.

"Come on," Max said without taking a seat. "Let's have it. What happened?"

The professor sat up straight in his seat and took a deep breath. "You're not going to believe it."

Max was getting impatient and the professor could sense it.

"OK. OK. Just have a seat first," said the professor. As

Max sat down and tried to relax, the professor began. "Like I said, you're not going to believe it. There was no concrete. It was pure dirt above the door all the way to the surface. The drill went through with no problem at all. I slid the cord of the goggles up through easily and was able to scan all around."

"And?" Max prodded as the professor stopped to catch his breath and refocus. "What did you see?"

"Nothing," the professor said.

"There's no such thing as nothing," Max corrected.

"I mean there were no buildings or signs of civilization at all. All I could see was green everywhere. I mean it was beautiful. It was greener than anything I've ever seen."

"Was the house there?"

"No," answered the professor. "No house, no roads, nothing man-made as far as I could see. From the look of the concrete around the room, it has to be way into the future. I can't explain it, but I'm super-psyched. I wish we could go ahead with the final phase right now."

Max smiled, but shook his head.

The professor knew they had to stick to the itinerary.

They locked up the house and walked out to their vehicles. It was already getting dark.

The professor decided to take one last stab. "I'm telling you the truth about what I saw."

Max was surprised by that comment. "I believe you."

"So it would be like a hiking trip. You like hiking, you told me."

Max smiled. "I know you don't want to do this alone. Maybe we should consider bringing someone else in, someone who would be eager to join you."

The professor thought, then shook his head. "I'll see you in a few days," he said as he got into his truck.

Max got into his truck also and began the drive home. The professor followed until his turn-off and Max continued on the narrow rural road. He knew the professor was scared to go it alone. He felt bad about that and even a little guilty.

Max tried to picture what the professor had described. It did seem tempting. *Where was civilization in the picture? How advanced were they?* A thousand questions ran through his mind as he imagined what lay ahead of the professor. But he was sure he was making the right decision.

Suddenly, something appeared to move in the woods off to the right ahead of Max's truck. He tried to peer through the darkness into the trees. He could see a turn-off coming up, but nothing else and figured he must have imagined it. Then, there was a streak of brown and then blackness.

***

Max opened his eyes slowly and tried to focus. It was as if he hadn't used his eyes for a while. As things began to become less blurry, he could make out his mom and Julie sitting in two chairs beside his bed. His bed? As he became more astute, he realized it was a hospital bed in a hospital room.

"Was it a deer?" asked Max, remembering the brown blur.

"Yeah," said Rollo, "a really drunk one."

Max turned to his other side and saw Rollo and wondered how you could be in the same room with Rollo and not notice him.

"I didn't see you."

"Yeah, I get that a lot," joked Rollo.

Julie laughed.

"So tell me exactly what happened," Max offered to anyone.

Julie responded. "A car ran a stop sign and hit you. The guy was intoxicated."

"Drunk as a skunk," Rollo embellished.

"How is he?" asked Max.

"Told you!" said Julie, pointing to Rollo. "I told you that would be his first question."

"Man, he came out unscratched like most drunks do," said Rollo.

Max breathed a sigh of relief. Then he thought about himself. "How did I come out?"

"You're lucky," his mom said.

"As opposed to everyone who wasn't involved in an auto accident last night?" Max joked.

Rollo laughed.

"Your seatbelt didn't lock and you hit the windshield," his mom said, attempting to clarify her assessment. "But they said you had no head trauma and x-rays could find no broken ribs. So basically, you ended up with a few bruises."

"I *was* lucky," Max said sincerely.

His mom smiled. Then she looked at Julie and smiled. Looking up at Rollo, she said, "I'm hungry. Rollo. Would you like to accompany me to the cafeteria?"

"Like I could ever say no to that," Rollo answered.

They walked out the door, leaving Max and Julie alone.

Max smiled a really big smile. He almost didn't care he was in an accident since it brought Julie here. "I'm so happy to see you."

Julie took his hand in hers. It was obvious that she was happy too. "I missed you so much."

"I know," said Max, "same here. But soon the fall semester will be here, and we'll be together every day after that."

"Will we?" A tear began to roll down her cheek. "What about the experiment?"

"Only a couple more days and that's over."

She smiled and leaned over and kissed him.

She stayed there all day and Max's parents were there on and off all day. Other visitors filtered in throughout the day until visiting hours were over. Max slept great that night and was ready to go home the next day.

The doctor looked him over one last time. "OK, you look good to me. Are you ready to go home?"

Max nodded. After two days in the hospital he was dying to get home.

"Should have you ready to go in an hour," the doctor said before leaving the room.

Max looked over at his dad who had walked in during the doctor's checkup. Julie had left earlier to go back home, and the professor had come earlier in the morning. It wasn't a terribly bad hospital stay as hospital stays go, but there's no place like home.

"How you feeling?" his dad asked.

"Great."

"Good," his dad smiled. "Got time for one more visitor?"

"Yeah. Sure. Who is it?"

His dad walked to the door and looked out into the hallway. "[illegible]m[illegible]on [illegible] s[illegible]n."

[illegible] g[illegible] w[illegible] k[illegible]d i[illegible]at [illegible]a[illegible] c[illegible]d[illegible]'t [illegible]e[illegible]g[illegible]. [illegible]w[illegible] b[illegible] t[illegible]i[illegible]y [illegible]ar [illegible]l[illegible] h[illegible]d [illegible]rim[illegible]e[illegible] b[illegible]a[illegible]d [illegible]n[illegible] r[illegible]a [illegible] a [illegible]v[illegible] p[illegible]e[illegible]te[illegible] pa[illegible] ar[illegible] l[illegible] bu[illegible] t[illegible]-u[illegible] sh[illegible]rt.

[illegible]'ll [illegible]v[illegible] y[illegible]u t[illegible] alo[illegible], h[illegible]s [illegible]a[illegible] s[illegible]d [illegible]e [illegible]c[illegible] wa[illegible] c[illegible]t.

[illegible]ax [illegible]o[illegible]e[illegible] at [illegible] g[illegible] w[illegible]it[illegible] c[illegible]n[illegible]i[illegible]or. T[illegible]h[illegible] y [illegible] h[illegible] hands in his pocket and was staring at the floor.

"Do I know you?" asked Max.

The guy looked up and it appeared to Max that he might begin crying any second.

"I'm the guy who hit you."

"Oh," said Max. "Are you okay?"

"Yeah," the guy laughed. "I am. I just feel so bad about what happened."

"It's okay," offered Max. "We were both lucky."

The guy nodded. "But I wanted you to know that's not normal for me. I guess I didn't realize how much I had to drink. I didn't even see the sign."

"The signs? What signs?" he asked, thinking about Julie and her signs.

"The stop sign," the guy said. "I didn't even see the stop sign. But yeah, that's a sign that you've had too much to drink when you can't even see the signs."

Max laughed.

"All I know for sure," the guy continued, "is that if I could go back in time, I'd change things. I'd not drink or at least make sure I didn't drive. I could have killed us both."

Max stared at the guy as his mouth dropped open. After a few seconds, he began to realize that his blank stare was making the guy uncomfortable.

"Say that again," Max commanded.

"I'm serious; I could have killed us both."

"No, not that," said Max. "Before that."

The guy looked confused as he tried to think about what he had said.

Max gave him a hint. "You said if you could go back in time. . ."

"Yes. Absolutely."

"People say stuff like that all the time," Max replied. "But would you really do something like that if you could?"

The guy nodded. "Are you kidding? Yes, I would. If I had a time machine, I would definitely go back in time to fix this. It would be a gift."

The guy apologized several more times and then left. Max was still staring out into space as his dad came back in.

"I think he's a good kid," his dad remarked. "And I really don't think he will drink and drive again."

Max returned his focus to the room and to his dad. "I think you're right on both counts."

26

Professor Nowak opened his front door after the doorbell rang.

"OK, we need to set strict guidelines for this first exploration," said Max.

"Yes, I agree," said the professor. "Come on in and we'll talk about it. How are you feeling?"

"Still a little sore but much better."

Max followed him to the small dining room where the professor shuffled some notebooks and old newspapers around for Max to have a clear spot to sit. The sunlight flooded through the [illegible text obscured]

revealed how long it had been since the last dusting.

The professor noticed it the same time Max did. "Maid's on vacation."

"For one thing," Max continued without acknowledging the maid joke, "the first time we need to adhere to a strict three-day limit."

"I agree again."

"No matter how excited we are or how much we want to go further, three days tops." Max was taking no chances that the professor was not understanding him.

The professor stared, looking dumbfounded. "Did you say 'we?' Oh my gosh. Are you serious?"

Max answered his question with a simple statement. "I have a backpack."

The professor was so relieved. "Whatever you say we'll stick to like glue."

They sat and talked and took notes for the first future exploration. It was only two weeks before the fall semester. Max was still on leave from work, so they both decided now was the time. They would tell everyone that they were going on a hiking trip, which was the truth. They would be gone from Friday through Sunday of the upcoming week since classes began on that upcoming Thursday. The three-day rule was the head of the list, meaning that they could not walk in any direction for more than a day and a half. If they never saw anything but grass, so be it. They agreed that each would take one can of mace for security. Neither owned a gun nor knew how to use one so they figured that was out. Another rule was that if either one of them wanted to cut the trip short for whatever reason, the other would not argue and come back with them willingly. Any sign of danger was an automatic deal-breaker and they would return pronto.

They sealed it with a handshake and Max got up and left.

***

That Friday morning, Max was headed out the door very early with his backpack in hand. He had told his parents of the three-day hiking trip, explained that the experiments with the professor were complete, and this was more for recreation before returning to school for fall classes.

His parents were not too thrilled; especially when Max told them that he would have his cell phone with him, but was certain there would be no signal where they were going. He promised to call them as soon as he got back in range to let them know everything was fine.

Julie also didn't seem too happy when he told her.

For those reasons, Max drove toward the old house in Michigan with a little sadness. But soon it would be over, and he could finally tell everyone what was going on. He hoped they would all forgive him after that.

Still, the excitement of what lay ahead of him this day was overwhelming. It was almost the feeling of Christmas Eve as a child, but magnified a hundred times. Max was glad he had decided to go and knew the professor was glad also.

Once again, the professor's truck was already there, and Max began to wonder if he slept there sometimes. He walked up to the front door, and the professor opened it ahead of him to let him in.

The professor had in his hands a manila folder about a half-inch thick with papers. "This is everything right here," he said, holding it up. Walking over to the basement door entrance, he showed Max where he had mounted a clear plastic file holder and placed the folder inside. "This explains every detail of time travel

[several lines obscured and illegible]

"Today's date is Friday, August 24th, 2012. If you come across this message before Monday the 27th, please do not tamper with anything. We are running an experiment on time travel. This is not a joke. If you find this sometime past the date listed here, then please make sure these notes get into the hands of

Dean Whittaker at Cedarbluff University
in Fulton County, Ohio.

"Nice touch on making sure they know it's not a joke," Max teased.

The professor laughed as he put the paper back in the folder. "So what's first?" he asked.

Max replied, "First, I want to run one test with all the equipment."

"Let's do it," said the professor.

They took both backpacks filled with clothes, sleeping bags, water, food, medicine, cameras, and mace and placed them in the time unit along with the drill, goggles, flashlight, and shovel. Walking back into the basement, they gave the generator a checking over. Not only did it supply the electricity for the lights and computers, it also sent the electrical current through the metal rods running through the time unit and also ran the battery chargers that kept the batteries running current through the wires wrapped around the metal rods. Everything depended on the generator, and the gas tank was filled to the top which they had calculated would allow the generator to run for several weeks, much longer than they would need.

They took their seats in the basement and ran the test with all the equipment. Like all the other tests, it went flawlessly.

They went out to the time unit to give it one last checkup. All the equipment seemed fine but Max noticed one problem. The professor had added the other scuba tank to the back wall and both of them seemed loose, especially the one that had been mounted the longest.

"Check this out," said Max as he showed the professor how loose the tanks were.

"That's from the vibration," said the professor. He walked back to the house and came back with a Phillips screwdriver and attempted to tighten the screws. But the ones on the older unit would not tighten because the holes had become too enlarged. He

walked back to the house again and came back with four longer
and thicker screws along with a cordless drill.

Max watched as he took one screw out at a time and replaced it with the larger and longer ones. The top screws were the
only ones that had become loose, and they screwed into the inside
wall of the time unit right at the very top. Max didn't like that they
were making last-minute changes, even though it was just simply
replacing screws but said nothing.

They walked back inside for one last checkup there and decided they were good to go. Climbing back down into the underground room, the professor stepped into the time unit first. He
turned to look at Max who had stopped right outside. The professor watched as Max scanned the entire machine and worried that
Max was getting cold feet.

But there was something that didn't seem right to Max. He
couldn't help but look at the metal rod running through the box.
He couldn't see the rods themselves because of the coated wire
covering them, but something was giving him a bad vibe.

"What's wrong?" asked the professor.

"I don't know," said Max, "just a bad feeling."

"It's nerves," reassured the professor. "I've been through the
exact same thing my first time."

Max climbed into the machine, and the professor squeezed
by but not to turn the machine and look at Max to make his way to
the reference machine and veered back around him to get to the

The professor flipped open the little plastic cover that he had
installed over the switch to make sure no one bumped it accidentally. He looked at Max to make sure he was ready.

Max said nothing.

"I need you to give me the go-ahead," the professor explained.

Max took a deep breath and said, "Do it."

The professor flipped the switch. The time unit shook so
hard that Max had to grab the sides to maintain his balance. Then,
it became still, but Max's ears were ringing like the professor had

mentioned, but louder than he thought would be the case.

He looked at the professor as the ringing began to subside and asked, "Is this what it was like before?"

The professor shook his head. "It wasn't quite like this. The vibration seemed stronger. Maybe it's because of the extra weight."

Max looked out through the opening in the hatch. The Plexiglass window was missing and it was dark on the other side. This meant they were there; they were in the future.

The professor got up and turned the wheel to unlock the hatch. He pushed it open and stepped out with his flashlight. Max followed. The underground room was intact but Max could tell the concrete blocks bore the signs of time.

"The hole is still here." said the professor pointing the flashlight at the plexiglass door in the ceiling. "I don't think we need the drill."

The professor took out the goggles and began to run the cord up through the hole just like he had done before. While the professor was doing that, Max held the flashlight for him. Then, he took his own flashlight and scanned it around the little room. Only the lead time unit was visible here in this time. The emitters, the rods, and the wires were all gone.

"Did you see this before?" asked Max as he pointed the flashlight to the side of the time unit.

The professor stopped feeding the cord through the hole. "What?" he asked as his eyes followed around to the left side of the lead unit where Max was aiming the light.

There on the ground was the camera that had been sucked off the wall during the first trial run. It was crumpled from impact.

Max walked over, picked it up, and looked at it.

"I never even looked back there," the professor said as he smiled and then turned to continue what he was doing. "OK, I'm through."

Max walked over and took the goggles since the professor was holding them out for him. Max slid them on and let the view come into focus. It was nothing but blue.

"You're looking straight up, Max. Turn the knob on the goggles to make the tip bend," Professor Nowak instructed.

Max did exactly that and was shocked. It was just like the professor described: green grass and green trees as far as he could see. The professor rotated the cord so Max could get a 360-degree view.

Max slid the goggles off and the professor laughed at his expression.

"Ready?" the professor asked.

Max nodded.

The professor unlocked the trap door, allowing it to swing downward. The dirt above it stayed intact. He began to pick away at it with the shovel as the rich dirt began to fall on the steps and floor of the underground room.

Max took his foot and raked it aside as it fell so that it didn't pile up there.

After the professor got about halfway through, the rest of it o' a se 1, ending a lot of dirt downward. The professor jumped a k u i ti e o v id b r l t.] : o lv udnly filled vi h r gł su l h'

(le rin ; f h r n i n g u s i ì ;t ie e h o es or kel o es p a l u e ñu u a ır p si o to te ;r u d 7 e l :j u el el m e u a l la w t e i a ve

Max stood t.e. ı f w e o s v l is p di] couldn't take his eyes off the blue sky and wondered where the professor was. Finally, he decided to follow when the professor stuck his head back over the hole.

"Send up the backpacks," he called down to Max.

Max went into the time unit and grabbed the packs. He handed them one by one to the professor who pulled them up and laid them on the ground. Max then climbed the steps and emerged.

Max couldn't believe his eyes. The landscape was amazing. He had never seen anything like it. The house was indeed gone, and all he could see was grass and trees all the way to the horizon. It was almost like a painting, and the artist decided to use only two colors. He looked over at the professor who was kneeling on the ground.

"This is unbelievable," said Max.

The professor agreed. "Feel this grass," he said.

Max knelt down and ran his fingers through the grass. It was like running his fingers through soft fur.

"It's got to be some kind of hybrid or engineered grass," the professor said as he plucked several strands and examined them. "All the blades are pointed so it doesn't look like it's been cut anytime recently. You would expect it to be waist-high but it's not."

Max smiled as he spun around slowly and took it all in. The grass was indeed the perfect height, and Max noticed that it not only ran up to the edge of the woods; it seemed to cover the forest floor as well.

The professor also seemed in awe, like a child in a candy store. He stood there motionless with his eyes half closed, his arms hanging effortlessly beside him, and breathed it all in.

Max smiled as he noticed the professor. He looked like a picture out of a wilderness magazine with his blue jeans rolled up twice into cuffs that revealed brand new hiking boots. He wore a dark green t-shirt cover by a sleeveless, tan hiking vest. His muscular arms filled out the sleeves well. They were not that huge, but well defined as the triceps protruded clearly. A very broken-in light-green baseball cap topped it off. The cap displayed a white "H" and Max wondered what that stood for. He assumed it was one of the professor's old softball caps but didn't ask.

Max realized his own attire was less than magazine worthy as he had thought of the trip as more of a grunge job and had worn old pants, a very faded button-up shirt, and his old tennis shoes. But Max wasn't concerned with appearances, especially after seeing the landscape. If they never took another step, Max would still be happy he came.

27

After putting on their backpacks, Max asked, "Which way?"

"Well," said the professor scouring the terrain, "there's a creek about a mile west of here called Beam Creek. I mean if it's still there. If we follow that due south, there was a small town called Morenci about five miles away. That would be the closest civilization in our time."

"Sounds like a good plan to me," Max said.

As they headed west, Max noticed that the sun was about halfway up the western sky, meaning they were walking directly _____ mid-afternoon. The
_____
_____
_____
_____
_____
way to describe it to in self, u i was al d ur sta le
made him think of the time that his dad had taken the ____ th to Six Flags Great America just outside of Chicago. Max was 12 years old. They had left early one morning while it was still dark and Max had slept all the way there. His parents woke him up when they were in the parking lot. As he stepped out of the truck, the sheer wonderment of the place hit him like a ton of bricks and he couldn't stop grinning. Now, in this place, Max had that same feeling. It was like a combination of magic and the surreal. There were no amusement park rides here at all; only grass, trees, and

sky as far as the eye could see, but it generated those same feelings, only much stronger.

About 45 minutes later, they came to the creek.

"Is this how you remember it?" asked Max.

The professor shook his head as he was at a loss for words. The stream looked beautiful. The water seemed so clear that the sunlight made it sparkle like diamonds. The soft grass went all the way to the water. The professor looked up at Max in amazement and shrugged his shoulders.

Max followed as the professor turned left to follow the creek southward. They walked along in silence for the next couple of hours as each soaked in the beautiful scenery.

They came up on some rocks, which were almost perfect cubes about two feet high. Stopping to rest, the professor sat on one of the rocks and Max did the same.

"Maybe there are cities in the sky like on the Jetsons," the professor said.

"Maybe," Max replied. "Maybe there are colonies on the moon or other planets."

The professor nodded. That made sense to him.

They each took their camera and snapped some pictures and then continued on. After several more hours, it was abundantly clear that the town of Morenci was nowhere to be found. And what was more disturbing was that there seemed to be no towns or roads anywhere. Although neither would say it out loud, neither could help but wonder if civilization or even humans existed anymore. *Had they finally killed themselves off?* These thoughts crept into their heads, but they fought them off.

Even though many hours had elapsed, the sun still seemed to linger in the sky. The professor noticed that Max kept looking at it also.

"The earth's rotation must be very different."

Max agreed. "Maybe we should think about getting some rest. Are you tired?"

The professor had to actually think about that. "I'm not

really tired, but a nap sounds great."

They took off their backpacks and sat on the grass. The grass was so soft that they didn't even unroll their sleeping bags and the temperature seemed a perfect 70 degrees. Max simply used the rolled up sleeping bag as a pillow and lay down. Within seconds he was fast asleep.

***

Max opened his eyes slowly. It was daylight, but he felt as if he had slept for 20 hours, and he wondered if night had come at all and they had slept through it. He felt great. He was half expecting to be cold when he awoke for no other reason than his metabolism slowing, but he was very comfortable. The grass was smooth and inviting and the fur blanket on his back was soft and warm.

Fur blanket?

He reached back behind him and felt the soft fur of something, something that moved as it breathed and had a heartbeat. Max was afraid to move. He looked over at the professor who was st   s   d

the professor had something better. He suddenly wished he had put the mace in his pocket before going to sleep, but wasn't sure how effective that would even be.

The professor apparently had the same idea as he slowly slid his backpack around in front of him and unzipped it to try to find the mace. As he fumbled around inside the pack, his camera slid out and fell onto the ground with a slight thud.

The fur blanket jumped. Then, it quickly stood up on all fours and towered above Max.

Max couldn't move. He had never seen a bear so large, even on TV. Of course, it could have been the angle at which he was currently viewing it.

The bear didn't seem to pay any attention to him, but simply stood there looking around. Then, it looked down and put its mouth right up against Max's face.

Max's brain started to work overtime as reason somehow seemed to occupy the space in his mind where fear should be. He knew you weren't supposed to run from a bear, but wondered how worse that outcome could be than a bear about to bite your head off. He was certain that he was doomed. He didn't want it to end this way, to travel to the future only to be eaten by a bear. He made up his mind. At the count of three, he was going to jump up and run.

One. . .

The bear took its tongue and began to lick Max's face. Then, as abruptly as it had gotten up, it trotted away.

Max sat up and then stood as he watched the bear go up the side of the creek until it was out of sight. "No way that just happened," he said with his heart racing.

The professor was at a loss for words.

"That's it," said Max. "We go back."

The professor looked at him as if he was confused.

"You know the rules," Max said. "Any sign of danger and we turn back."

"I know the rules," said the professor, "but to go back means we go in the same direction the bear just went."

Max laughed. It was a sad laugh, the laugh that is created when panic and logic collide. As much as he wanted to go back, he didn't want to follow the bear. He looked at the professor for guidance and noticed he was in deep thought, like a man trying to solve a puzzle.

"I think I figured it out," the professor said.

Max wasn't even sure which puzzle of the endless ones here he was referring to.

The professor explained. "OK, look at how green every-thing is, and there are no roads or buildings. Now take that bear; it was huge."

Max certainly didn't argue that point.

"But bears only get that large when they're putting on fat to hibernate for the winter." The professor held his arms out to each side. "This is definitely not winter. And the bear had a very clean coat and didn't seem to be afraid of humans. Right?"

Max was listening, but had no idea where this was going.

"I'll bet this is a wildlife preserve or something."

As the professor finished explaining his theory, a large white-tailed doe and a beautiful little fawn came out of the woods and walked right past them to the creek. The fawn drank from the stream as the mother looked on.

"I think you might be onto something," Max said.

The fawn began to splash around as it played in the stream. The mother stood there as if she had no worries in the world.

Max walked slowly toward her.

She looked directly at him, but didn't flinch.

Max cont[...]ued [...] was al[...] t[...] fe[...] and then
l[...] is ppr[...]c[...] i[...] cl[...]s[...] c[...] [...]e[...] g e[...]
i[...]d[...]f wa[...]ing n[...] [...] he[...] r[...] n ir[...] t[...] t[...] m [...]h[...]
c[...] e[...] he he[...] t[...] x[...] b st[...] g[...] t[...] n[...] p t
h[...] [...]a[...] a[...] ru he[...] [...]w te[...] er[...] d[...] a[...] is h n[...]s
h t[...] sp[...] s sl[...] v[...] l[...] [...]la[...] u[...]gh[...] s[...] h[...] ht[...] o[...] t
Deuce the hamster.

"Let me guess," said the professor. "Soft fur?"

"Very."

The fawn, not to be left out, rushed over and extended its own head for Max.

The professor stared in awe as the two deer competed for Max's attention.

Finally having enough, they slowly turned and walked back into the woods.

Max suddenly felt better as the encounter with the bear took a backseat to this encounter.

"This is not a good sign," said the professor.

"Why?"

"Animals should be afraid of humans," he explained. "Think of any Discovery special you've ever seen where animals were not afraid of humans. It's always in a location where they've never seen humans. So even if this was a wildlife preserve, these animals should at least be familiar with humans."

Max thought about what that could mean.

"Then there's the sky," said the professor.

"What about it?"

"It's empty." The professor pointed upward. "We haven't seen or heard one plane or any flying machine. There are no jet trails or any sign at all of air travel."

Max hadn't realized it, but the professor was right. It was one thing to not come across a road because that could simply mean that they weren't near a town. But to not see any sign of people flying was another thing. Still, he tried to push back the thoughts that mankind might not even exist anymore and turned to walk onward along the creek.

The professor followed.

As they walked, they heard a strange sound coming from the forest. It almost sounded like a duck, but had a much deeper tone that lasted for at least five seconds each time. They peered into the woods to try to get a look.

"What is it?" asked the professor.

"I don't know."

"It doesn't sound too vicious. Want to check it out?"

Max looked back at the professor and smiled. "What is the sound of vicious?"

The professor smiled at the question and then walked into the woods to find the source.

Max waited.

The professor was almost out of Max's sight when he called out. "I found it. It's okay. Come check it out."

Max followed the professor's path and walked up beside him. There, stretching his neck out for the professor to pet him, was a large bird of some sort. Max couldn't help but laugh when he saw it. It was kind of silly looking and its head made quick nodding motions as it tried to keep the professor's attention.

"What in the world is that?"

The professor turned to stare at Max with the oddest look on his face. It was the look of disbelief coupled with the look of someone who just found a long-lost relative.

Max smiled. "What? What is it?"

The professor looked back at the bird as to clarify himself before he said it out loud. "It's a dodo bird."

"A dodo bird?"

The professor nodded.

Max looked confused. "The bird that's been extinct for like a hundred years back in our time?"

The professor smiled. "More like 500 years."

Max looked at the odd bird. He hadn't seen a picture of one in a long time, but it looked right and he believed the professor.

[illegible] the professor, obvi- [illegible]

dodo bird could just suddenly exist again. But it is possible th[illegible] any DNA was ever found. . ."

"Cloning," Max whispered.

"It's the only answer I can think of." The professor seemed to be convinced, and it made him feel confident that humans were still in charge. "It would only make sense that huge strides have been made in cloning."

That made Max feel better, too. They gave their friend one more pat on the head and walked back out to the stream and continued on their way. They had gone about fifty feet when the professor stopped.

"What am I thinking? Hold on."

Max watched as the professor turned back. "What are you doing?"

"I gotta get a picture of that guy," the professor called out as he disappeared into the woods.

Max stood there waiting until the professor returned.

The professor walked up with a smile. "It dawned on me that all the pictures we've taken don't really prove anything. People can simply claim we went hiking in a beautiful area. But a picture of a dodo bird will raise some eyebrows."

"Sure you don't just want to take him back with us?"

The professor stopped to think.

"I'm joking," Max explained.

The professor smiled. "I just hope we see more extinct animals."

Max added, "If we see a T. Rex, I'm outta here."

Hours and hours passed again with no sign of humans, with only the occasional brush with nature. They had seen all kinds of birds, small forest animals like rabbits and raccoons, more deer, the dodo, and, of course their encounter with Gentle Ben.

Max was a little worried that they couldn't even tell how long they had been here. They each had worn a watch, but neither one of them had worked since climbing out of the hole, and neither Max nor the professor knew exactly how long they had slept. It was feasible to assume that they were nearing the halfway mark, but M   re ll d   pe r

Ve ed th   a u e g   e r r   he ba   "

Max   l.

ne on fo or pj l. I sn re t e da et.

A   you re

he p of o e d n   o t k .   at')o

wei

"What's weird," Max clarified, "is that the sun is still in exactly the same position as when we climbed out of the ground."

"I know." The professor stared at the sun. "Maybe it's like the areas close to the North Pole, you know, like those areas that have six months of daylight. Maybe the pole of the earth has shifted and it's closer to where we are now."

Max nodded as he thought about it. "I guess that's possible, but it seems like if that were the case, it would be colder here."

"Maybe the poles are not at the extremes like they used to

be," the professor offered.

They came to an area where the creek got a little wider, and Max took off his backpack and walked to the edge of the water.

The professor took his off as well and sat on the grass and leaned back against a tree. "See any fish?"

"No," Max said, "just gold."

The professor laughed, but stopped when Max turned around with a serious look on his face. He got up and quickly walked over to the stream.

The clearness of the water still refracted the sunlight rays into beautiful arrays of light. But on the floor of the creek, a variety of different-colored smooth rocks adorned the creek bed in an almost perfect mosaic. Among the smooth stones were several that had a golden hue.

The professor reached down into the water, picked one up, and held it in front of him. He took a pocket knife from his pocket and began to scrape over the surface of the rock, and each swipe of the knife left its own indention.

"Is it real?" Max asked as he stared in wonderment.

"I believe so." The professor waded out a little ways into the water and scooped up several more of the gold rocks. "We should take these back for testing."

Max laughed. "Finally, I found something to motivate you into returning."

The professor smiled.

"Seriously, though," Max added. "Maybe we should call it a successful first trip and go back. Then we can plan a second trip when we have a lot more time."

"You're right," said the professor. "We can always come back." He walked over to grab his backpack and as he slid it on, he froze.

Max followed his gaze to see what had made him stop. About a hundred yards away was a man who appeared to be fishing.

The professor turned to look at Max and then they both

ducked behind a tree.

"Do you think he saw us?" asked Max.

Suddenly they could hear the man yelling. "Hey, guys. Come on out."

"I think he saw us," answered the professor, but he still didn't move.

Max peeked around his tree. "He's waving in this direction."

The professor slowly and cautiously stepped out from behind the tree and waved back. He began walking toward the man so Max followed. They walked up to the bank of the creek and nodded to the fellow.

The guy was standing in the middle of the creek with his pants legs rolled up to his knees to keep them dry. He was dressed in what appeared to be clothes from the 40s. He wore brown trousers, a white pull-over half-sleeve shirt that resembled old long johns, and he wore suspenders.

With that image and the dodo bird, Max began to wonder if they really had traveled forward in time.

"Hey, guys," the man said as he cast his fishing line from his fly-fishing pole, watching it land far in the stream. "You ever do any fly-fishing?"

Max and the professor shook their heads.

"Oh, you gotta try it," the man said with a laugh. "I think it's the most relaxing thing. By the way, my name is Gilbert."

He extended his hand and Max and the professor took turns shaking it and introducing themselves.

"Is this a wildlife preserve?" asked the professor.

The man looked at them as if it was an odd question. Then he thought for a second and replied, "Yes, yes it is."

"Is this your property?" asked Max.

"Oh no," the guy said. "I just fish here."

"Can you tell me how far it is to the nearest town?"

"No, I'm sorry," replied Gilbert.

Max and the professor looked at each other as if trying to

understand that response.

"Where do you live?" asked Max.

"Nearby," Gilbert replied with a smile.

The professor was beginning to get a little frustrated. "But not in a town?"

Gilbert shook his head.

Max tried to keep the mood light. "You prefer the country?"

Gilbert smiled again. "I enjoy everything, but yes, this country is beautiful. Don't you agree?"

They both nodded as they again looked around to absorb the incredible scenery.

"Is this still Michigan or Ohio?" asked Max.

"Or even the United States of America?" added the professor.

Gilbert smiled again and shook his head.

"What country is it?" asked Max.

Gilbert had to think a few seconds. "God's country?" he said almost as a question.

The professor smiled as he remembered a student from Tennessee who used that same expression to describe his home. He looked at Max and raised his eyebrows as if to ask if they should explain things to Gilbert.

Max thought Gilbert seemed harmless enough so he gave him a slight nod.

"Gilbert," the professor began, "Can I ask you a really strange question?"

Gilbert laughed. "Those are the most fun, aren't they?"

The professor decided being blunt was the most effective way. "What year is this?"

Gilbert looked confused. "I don't know."

"How could you not know?" asked Max.

"We don't go by calendar years if that's what you are referring to," explained Gilbert.

"The reason I ask," continued the professor, "is that Max

and I have come here from the year 2012."

Gilbert looked amazed.

"In a time machine of sorts," Max clarified.

"You're pulling my leg," Gilbert said.

Both Max and the professor shook their heads.

"Isn't that something?"

"So we're wondering," the professor added, "how far into the future we've come. You say you don't go by calendar years anymore, but can you at least give us an idea of how long ago the year 2012 was from now."

Gilbert thought for a second and said, "At least 1200 years ago." He began to count on his fingers. "Well, it would be over 1200 years."

Max and the professor looked at each other and smiled. They knew it had to be a long time into the future and now that theory was validated.

"How long have you guys been hiking?" Gilbert asked.

"A good while," answered the professor.

"You guys thirsty?"

He my ocked h s Gil t l ded them each a wooden
o l d it va la o d e i t s b o t
n to n u tl r v i n, ar u he wl d
lr k

Oh ny s Ta so d

T e ro ss t k ri s . lo Th e e
wate ve v a l. a s ?

"Water," Gilbert replied.

"I know, but I assume it's a manufactured brand," explained the professor. "So I wondered what they did to it or put in it."

Gilbert looked confused again.

"Where did this come from?" asked Max.

Gilbert pointed to the creek.

Max looked at the stream. He couldn't believe it. "Oh my goodness. You could make a fortune with this water."

The professor thought of another question. "Do you still

use money?"

Gilbert smiled and shook his head.

Max laughed. "This is like Star Trek. They didn't use money in the future either."

"Do you mind us asking you these questions?" the professor asked.

Gilbert smiled. "Oh, heck no. Ask away. I'm enjoying your company."

The professor thought for a moment as to how to word the next question. Then he asked, "In 2012, the population of the earth was around eight billion people. What is the population now?"

"I'm not exactly sure," said Gilbert, "but it's considerably less."

"Are there colonies on the moon or other planets?" asked Max.

Gilbert shook his head.

"But space travel has progressed?" the professor inquired.

"No," said Gilbert. "We don't concern ourselves with those things anymore."

"So much for Star Trek," Max scoffed.

The professor looked so confused. "I just figured this far into the future that civilization would have grown a lot, and that the whole planet would be concrete and buildings with flying cars and stuff like that."

Gilbert stared at the professor as if he couldn't believe what he was hearing. "You thought that?" he asked as if he knew the professor and this didn't seem right.

The professor nodded. "I think everyone thinks that from our time," he clarified.

"Well, they're wrong as you can see," Gilbert affirmed.

As the professor and Max pondered what had happened in the world, Gilbert collected his fishing rod and lures and walked over to a rocky area.

"Let's grab a seat, fellows. I want to hear more about this time travel."

The professor and Max each found a seat on the rocks and told Gilbert how they had accidentally discovered the way to make lead heavier and that had led to the time travel. Gilbert amazed them as he seemed to understand what they were saying about wormholes and the fourth dimension. He seemed to have the intelligence to grasp the concept, which is one reason they wondered why the future was not more advanced.

"OK," Max said, trying a new angle. "Can you explain to us what a typical day would be for you?"

Gilbert laughed. "I don't think I can answer that one. I don't even know what typical would be."

"We've noticed the sun," said the professor. "Does it always stay right there this time of year?"

Gilbert looked at the sun and held his hand over his eyes as to form a visor. "Yep, always there."

"So are there towns and cities like there used to be?" asked the professor.

"There are no structures that make up cities if that's what you mean." Gilbert was really trying to be helpful.

29

Max and Professor Nowak followed Gilbert as he walked along without a care in the world. With his pants legs still rolled up, his old-timer's suspenders, and with the fishing pole over his shoulder much like a kid would do, Max thought he looked like something out of a Norman Rockwell painting.

The professor nudged Max as they walked and motioned up ahead. Max followed the professor's gaze and saw what he saw. On the opposite side of the creek was a grassy hill, and over the top of that hill was a kite floating in the wind. As they got closer, other kites filled the sky. Then they could see people and hear laughter.

Soon they could see picnic tables and people sitting and standing around and lots of children playing with kites and other toys. So serene was the image that it made Max and the professor smile.

Gilbert led them to a wooden bridge that seemed to be hand-carved out of a single tree. He walked across and Max and the professor followed. As they neared the picnic tables, which also seemed to be hand-carved instead of pieced together, everyone stopped what they were doing and smiled at them.

Gilbert asked them to take a seat and announced to everyone in ear shot that he brought some guests. Everyone greeted them, and most came by to shake hands or pat them on the back. It was almost as if they were the honored guests that everyone had been waiting to show. Two kids, a little boy and a little girl about eight years old, came up and sat beside Max, and the boy handed him a hand-carved wooden tractor.

Max smiled at the object in his hands. When he tried to return it, however, the kids simply smiled and jumped up and ran back to play with the other kids.

An older woman walked up on the other side of the table and said, "Hey, guys. I'm Amelia. Are you two hungry?"

Max and the professor looked at each other and wondered why they weren't, or at least why they hadn't been before now. They had brought food, but had not once stopped to eat and they knew it had at least been the better part of a day. But now that she asked, they were starving. They took off their backpacks and sat them on the ground next to their chairs.

"I guess our adrenaline is pumping so fast we didn't even think about food," the professor said to Max.

Max nodded, but wasn't sure he believed that.

Amelia came back with a plate of bread and set it in front of them. The professor and Max thanked her and wondered if they _____ go ahead or wait on the main meal. But Amelia simply _____ _____ for _____ to eat.

_____ _____ _____ she said as if that was wha_ was

_____ ing

_____ the ma_n cour_e and eac_ _tore

_____ it_. It _as _ike t_e w_ter Both

_____ _____ y realiz_d this v_as _h_ be_ thing

they had _____ _____

"Oh my goodness," said the professor. "W_at's _n t_ _? It's like the water. I mean, is it chemically enhanced?"

"No chemicals at all," Gilbert said as he walked back up and took a seat across from them. "There are no chemicals in any-thing anymore. That's why the water tastes so good."

"And the grass and trees?" asked Max.

Gilbert nodded. "No more chemicals in anything."

The professor finished eating the piece of bread and decided to press Gilbert. "You are a very kind and hospitable guy, Gilbert, and we appreciate you taking us in like this. But we really need to know what happened in the world. Can you please give us a condensed version of what all has transpired since the year 2012?"

Max stopped chewing and looked at Gilbert for a reaction.

Gilbert looked around at all the people standing or sitting nearby and smiled. They all smiled back, and the ones sitting got up as everyone turned to walk away.

Max felt for a minute that they had offended them as he watched everyone, including the children, walk over the hill and out of sight. But looking back at Gilbert made him feel better as he was smiling very gently toward them.

"You guys know what it was like in 2012 with all the killing, wars, starvation, and disease?"

Max and the professor nodded.

"It got worse," Gilbert continued. "It gets much worse. Finally, in the year of our Lord 2224, well, let's just say it was literally the year of our Lord."

Max and the professor both looked confused.

Gilbert went on. "That's the year that God had enough and Jesus returned."

"Oh my," said Max.

"The second coming?" asked the professor.

Gilbert nodded.

"Then what happened?" asked the professor.

"You know the rest," Gilbert stated. "Jesus gathered up the chosen ones, some of whom were alive when he returned, and they reigned with him for 1000 years. When that reign was over, the earth was pure again just like it began with Adam and Eve. Everyone was called back for judgment, and those of us whose names were found written in the book of life were spared the lake of fire and inherited eternal life. Then, Satan was cast into the fire and destroyed and then the beast."

Max and the professor sat frozen with their mouths open.

"I'm not sure why you guys are so shocked. You have spent most of your lives telling people this very thing would happen."

Max and the professor realized what Gilbert was saying was true. They had always told people that the second coming would most likely be soon. How, then, did they come to convince themselves that science fiction movies trumped their Christian beliefs?

Max finally snapped out of it. "What was the beast?"

Gilbert smiled. "The beast was God's wrath and judgment. Just like he allowed himself to die on the cross, he also let a part of himself be destroyed to fulfill his promise of salvation. There is no wrath or judgment anymore. There is no hate, anger, jealousy, pettiness, et cetera. There is nothing but peace, harmony, compassion, and love — forever."

"But this is really the earth?" asked the professor.

"Yes, this is the physical earth. It's just been made new."

"What about you, Gilbert? Are you a physical person?" Max asked.

He smiled again. "Let's just say that I wouldn't bleed if I cut myself shaving."

Max looked more confused. "But you shave?"

Gilbert laughed. "No. I'm sorry. Bad example."

questions kept coming to the professor.

that when

But

cause none of us remember judg...

straight here."

"Why don't you remember judgment day?" the professor asked.

"Remember, there's nothing negative anymore. And that day might have been very traumatic so, hence, not something we think about."

"But is this Heaven or earth?" asked Max.

"Both." Gilbert tried to think of a way to explain. "Think

of an old kingdom in medieval times. You had the entire kingdom spread out where the citizens of that kingdom lived. Then, you had the castle, which is where the king and his court lived. The earth is the kingdom of Heaven, just as it was the kingdom of Hell when Satan reigned. So to answer your question, this is the earth and it is Heaven."

"So which denomination was right?" asked the professor. "I mean, which one was the closest to being right?"

Gilbert looked down and slowly shook his head. He looked back up with a somber expression. "It was never about denominations. It was never even about being right. It was always about faith."

The professor let those words sink in. "So a person's deeds were not important?"

Gilbert's eyes got very big. "How can a person's deeds not be important? A person's actions define them whether they're a Christian or not. It's been that way since the beginning of time. In fact, look at Adam and Eve. Eve had faith, but like a lot of people who came after her, when she was tempted, her faith became weak. We know this by her actions. Faith is not about sitting back and having happy thoughts. It wasn't in the brick-and-mortar buildings or in the money you placed in the collection plates. It was always right here." Gilbert took his right hand and tapped on the left side of his chest.

"Do you remember your life before you died?"asked Max.

"Oh, of course," Gilbert said. "You remember everything. And what's more, if you have a favorite moment like a baseball game or first date or whatever, you can go back and relive it as many times as you want. You can see your kids or grandkids born again. Even here, you can be whatever age you want to be for as long or short a time as you want to be. If you want to be ten years old, you can be."

Max thought about all the kids that were here earlier and wondered how many were actually adults when they died.

"What about friends and loved ones that didn't make it?"

asked the professor. "Isn't that a sad thing?"

"There is no sad. We remember all the great things about them and now know great things about them we never knew. And like I said, we can go back and forth in time to relive any part of it. Time no longer exists. There is no time in eternity. You say you two came here in a time machine. The truth is, everyone came here from a different time. We are all time travelers to an extent, just not like you guys."

The professor was amazed at Gilbert's logic.

For hours they continued to ask questions ,and Gilbert never seemed to tire of them. Coming here the way they had almost made them feel like trespassers, but no one said anything. But when they really thought about it, what was someone going to say? No one in Heaven was going to yell at them or try to run them off, so what other reaction could they possibly expect?

"What about God?" Max asked.

"That's a very good question," Gilbert said with a big smile. "But what is the question?"

Max laughed. "Do you ever see Him or angels or anything

Max and the professor couldn't help but smile at his heartfelt reply.

For many more hours, Gilbert walked around with them, answered questions, and introduced them to others and made them feel that their presence here was as welcomed as anyone's. Then he left them alone to explore, mingle, or whatever they wanted to do.

Max and the professor walked along, taking in the beautiful scenery and clicking pictures here and there.

As they stopped to click some pictures of a beautiful parrot who seemed interested in their presence, the professor said, "The problem is, I don't even know how long we've been here, but I do know we should probably start back soon."

Max nodded. "I agree completely. I mean, it's a wonderful place, but we have to get back to our lives. My mom and dad will be worried if we're not back when I told them we would be. And we both have the fall semester coming up."

"It *is* a wonderful place." The professor scanned the entire horizon and took a deep breath and released it with a sigh of contentment. "I think I might just stay here. Just tell everyone when you get back."

Max knew he was joking, but played along. "Sure. Give me the gold rocks before I go."

They both laughed.

✥ 30 ✥

Later on, Max and the professor separated for a while. Professor Nowak walked around with Gilbert, asking more questions while Max flew kites and played with the children.

"Fly mine, Uncle Max," said a little girl as she handed him her kite string.

Max chuckled at the title. Of course, he had never been an uncle so the term of endearment was very welcomed. He handed the string of one kite back to the little boy to whom it belonged and took the new one from his newly crowned niece who now danced

[text obscured]

and not the adults, so he sought out the professor.

Gilbert and Porfessor Nowak were sitting on wooden benches, one on each, which rested under a huge tree with a canopy that was at least a hundred feet wide. As he neared them, he could see that Gilbert was holding his arms out as far as he could beside him and a little over his head.

"The one that got away?" Max asked as he walked up.

Gilbert laughed.

"He was telling me about angels," said the professor. "Oh,

and you gotta hear this."

"What?" asked Max as he sat beside the professor.

"Tell him, Gilbert."

Gilbert looked at Max. "I was telling Ronald here that you can now walk around the entire earth."

"And you've done it how many times?" The professor asked even though he knew, but wanted Max to hear.

Gilbert held up both hands with all ten fingers.

Max looked confused so Gilbert explained. "The oceans and seas do not exist anymore so you can literally walk around the world if you like. And I highly recommend it. It's breathtaking."

"And more animals?" asked Max.

Gilbert nodded. "Yes. Absolutely."

Max looked confused.

"What is it?" Gilbert asked.

"Does this mean animals have souls? I thought it took a soul to be granted salvation." Max thought for a second, then added, "I know it says in Isaiah 11:6 that the wolf shall dwell with the lamb and the leopard shall lie down with the kid. I guess I just wasn't sure what that meant."

Gilbert tried to think how best to form his next sentences. "I don't think an animal has a soul, but they have God's spirit. They are a creation of God and, therefore, paradise would not be complete without them. But they are like us now in that they no longer have material needs, so you can run with a cheetah if you like or even sleep with a bear."

Max laughed out loud as he looked over at the professor, knowing he must have told Gilbert about their experience.

They chatted for a while longer and then Gilbert excused himself again and left them to their thoughts.

As they were talking, they hadn't even noticed that a woman had sat on the bench only a few feet across from them. They only noticed when she spoke.

"Hey, guys."

Startled, they both looked up to see a smaller, older woman

sitting there. She had straight, grey shoulder-length hair and a beautiful smile.

"Hello," they both said in unison.

"Gilbert wanted me to come by and ask you about something," she said.

"What is it?" asked Max.

"Well, since you're here," she said, "there are some people here from your lives who want to see you."

They stared at each other. That thought had never occurred to them.

"Couldn't that have an effect on the past?" the professor asked. "I mean if we know who makes it and, more importantly, who doesn't, wouldn't we use that to try and save those."

"How is that different from how you both lived your lives? Didn't you always try to save others?"

Once again, the logic stumped the professor.

"This is optional, guys. It's up to you," the woman explained. "Gilbert just asked me to tell you about it because of my connection to both of you."

[text obscured] and Max stared at each other to

[text obscured]

visible glasses onto her face. Her hair slowly [obscured] to red and lots of prominent freckles appeared.

"Julie," Max said as he got up and hugged her.

She hugged him tight. Then, she walked over and hugged the professor and then took her seat again. She looked at them for several seconds with a big smile on her face. "Time travel? So that was the big secret. That's what you guys were working on?"

They both displayed a sheepish grin and Max could feel himself blushing.

Max was so happy to see Julie. It had only been a few days since he had seen her, but seeing her here, and as an older woman, made it seem like a lifetime ago.

The three of them chatted for what felt like hours. Julie seemed so glad to discuss the good old days, which, for Max and the professor, were recent events. But it was fun for all three of them.

"Did . . . uh?" Max wanted to ask about them as a couple, where it had progressed. Had they continued to date? Had they gotten married, had kids, etc.?

The professor and Julie watched as Max shuffled his feet around on the ground without finishing his question.

Max couldn't do it. Maybe it was from a sense of accountability since great literature has taught us that knowing the future could affect the future. Or maybe he was just too faint-hearted. "Did you have a good life?" he asked.

Julie smiled and closed her eyes. "I had a wonderful life. I lived for 86 years and I couldn't have asked for a better life. I didn't even know how incredible it was until I got here and could see it all at once. I have so many events that I revisit, and it multiplies the incredible joy that I already feel."

Max and the professor looked on and smiled as Julie seemed to be swept away with her own disclosure.

Julie opened her eyes and looked at Max. "I have relived a certain event on your parents' sofa many times."

Max grinned and blushed.

The professor's mouth dropped open. "Hey. Give us some details here. Should the children leave the room?"

Julie laughed. "No, silly. I'm talking about our first kiss. We had no clue what we were doing, but it was a magical moment."

"That it was," Max confirmed.

There was a moment of silence as they all just seemed to let the flavor of the atmosphere soak in.

"Did you guys end up together?" the professor blurted out.

It was Max's turn to let his mouth drop open as he looked over at his friend with disbelief.

The professor realized his breach of etiquette and shrugged his shoulders to try to cover his guilty look.

"There are certain things we probably shouldn't discuss." Julie smiled at the professor to show him there were no hard feelings. Then, she added, "Like you winning the Nobel Prize for example."

The professor's eyes opened wide. "Really? I do?"

"I don't know," answered Julie, "I'm just saying that would be a good example."

Max laughed as did the professor. He recognized that little devious smile that Julie now displayed. He remembered it from his time. It was so good to see that her wonderful personality and sense of humor were still the same. As Max thought about it, however, he realized it was more these qualities than the physical appearance that makes a person who they are, so it only makes sense that you would still have these traits here.

"OK, here's the deal," she said, finally getting down to
u   r   y   had any connection to at all in life
v   n   e   d   u   r
c   n   v   c   e   y   o   n
A   d   c   d   d   ed   s.   e ip
y   n   e
                 1e   l   y   le   v   lo
            n   fe   e

"What about my parents?" asked

"I'm sorry. I don't have a list," corrected Julie. "I only know about Max's family because I was connected to them in life." Looking back at Max, she added, "And your little sister is here."

"I don't have a sister."

Julie smiled. "Didn't your mom ever tell you about. . ."

"About the miscarriage?" asked Max.

Julie nodded.

"And she's here?"

"Of course she's here," replied Julie. "So like I said, this is optional. So what do you say, guys?"

They both agreed, so Julie got up and told them she would arrange it and walked away.

"Can you believe this?" asked the professor. "We travel 1200 years into the future to meet people from our past."

When he put it that way, Max realized how odd it sounded.

"Let's agree on something," the professor added. "When this part is over, let's head back."

Max agreed completely. "We have to. I don't even know how long we've been here. It could easily have been a week already."

The professor nodded. "I think it might be longer even. But think of the stories we're going to be able to tell people. Can you imagine what they'll think? No way anyone will believe us without proof," the professor added.

Not hearing a response, he looked over at Max and what he saw took his breath away. Max was staring off into the distance with a strange look on his face. It was the look of sudden realization, the look a man might have who boards a plane and realizes he left the stove on. The professor turned to look in the direction of Max's stare in case it was actually something physical he was seeing. Seeing nothing but the beautiful landscape, he turned back to Max.

"Max? Hey, your face is going to freeze that way."

Max didn't seem to hear the professor's joke.

Waving his hands in front of Max's face, he tried again. "Earth to Max. Come in Max."

Max slowly turned his gaze back toward the professor, but his focus was still somewhere far behind him. In a voice barely above a whisper, he muttered, "Why didn't she know?"

31

Dean Whittaker sat behind his desk and searched all over for a stapler. "Is there a sprite or something that comes in between every semester to rearrange or hide all our staplers?"

Ms. Fulmer, the dean of students, laughed. She walked over and tried to help him find one.

His receptionist entered the office. "Dean Whittaker, there's a woman here to see you. She says she's the mother of one of our students."

"Of course. Show her in."

[text obscured by scan damage]

Max's mom eased down into one of the large easy chair backs. It completely consumed her small frame. She sat quietly, almost as if she was in church, as she seemed to be waiting for permission to speak.

"What can I do for you?"

She looked right into the dean's eyes. "My son is missing."

The dean's heart sank at those words. Suddenly, finding a stapler was not important, as he could see in her eyes the seriousness of her concerns. It gave him chills as he thought about the time where he had lost his five-year-old daughter in the supermarket and the ensuing panic it had caused. Turning to Ms. Fulmer, he asked, "Betty, can you find Charlie for me?"

Ms. Fulmer nodded and left the office.

"Charlie is our head of security," he explained. "At what dorm does your son live?"

"He lives at home."

The dean was confused. "I don't understand. Classes don't start until tomorrow so why would you come here? He shouldn't be here until tomorrow."

"I know," she explained, "but he's been working with Professor Nowak all summer, and now I think they're both missing."

The dean tried to let that soak in. Ms. Fulmer entered again with Charlie.

Charlie walked to the dean's desk and stood almost at attention to find out what was required of him. His security uniform and badge made him look like a police officer to Max's mom. Combined with his muscular arms, square jaw, and dark complexion, he certainly looked qualified to be in security or perhaps even a bodyguard or bouncer.

"What's your son's name?" the dean asked.

"Johnny Maxwell, but he goes by Max."

"OK, all the faculty members are supposed to be here today. Charlie, send someone down to get Professor Nowak." Looking back at Max's mom, he asked, "Do you know any students he was friends with here?'

She gave him Julie and Rollo's names, and he instructed Charlie to send someone to try to find them as well.

"Tell me everything you know," he told Max's mom.

She laid out everything from the first time Max came to orientation to how much time he spent with the professor over the summer to the professed hiking trip that was supposed to be over Sunday, four days ago.

The dean began to realize how serious this was. It was compounded when Charlie walked back in.

"The professor is not here and his truck is not in the parking lot."

The dean stared at Charlie as if his words didn't register, so Charlie nodded to reaffirm what he had just said.

Dean Whittaker swallowed hard and shook his head. "Have you spoken to the sheriff?" he asked, looking back at Max's mom.

"Yes. I went there first."

"Let's see if they have any info. Grace!" he called out.

His receptionist walked in.

"Grace, get me the number to the Fulton County Sheriff's office."

Another security officer walked in with Rollo and Julie. When Julie saw Max's mom, she ran over to her and hugged her, which caused both of them to start crying.

Grace retuned with the number, and the dean began to dial, glad to have something to do to distract himself from the sad scene of the two women.

"Hello. Can I speak with Sheriff Furgerson? Yes, tell him it's Dean Whittaker of Cedarbluff University."

's   st ed crying to listen.

l   e   an over here at Cedarbluff nd. .

s   's t a problem. Thank you."

r   e   s staring at the dean wond ering

sh

e   looks and filled them in. "The sheriff does   or ation. He's sending a depu y over here and, in fact, he should be here any second. He wa ts the professor's address so he can go by and check his house. And I think he wants to talk to you two," he said, nodding toward Julie and Rollo.

The deputy came in a few moments later. "I need to see the professor's classroom and office, and I need an address to his residence."

"Charlie," the dean said, "take the deputy to Professor Nowak's office. Stop by and have Grace give you his home address."

The deputy turned to look at Mrs. Maxwell. "We're going to do everything we can, ma'am. We have your phone number so the best thing you can do is go home and wait by the phone, for either your son or us to call you." Then he looked at Julie and Rollo. "You guys are his friends?"

They nodded.

"Do you know where the sheriff's office is?"

"I do," said Rollo.

"It would be helpful if you could go over there and make a statement," he said.

They said they would.

The ball was rolling, but the dean wished he could do more. He felt really bad as he watched Max's mom walk slowly out of the office.

Julie tried to offer words of encouragement as she walked her out to the plumbing truck. But it was the blind leading the blind, as she also felt completely helpless and scared to death as she wondered what could have happened. After Max's mom drove away, she walked to her car with Rollo and he navigated for her until they arrived at the sheriff's office.

The front-desk officer walked them back to the sheriff's personal office. It was cluttered with paperwork, piles of paperwork, stacked on every flat surface in his office. The tops of the bookcase, the file cabinet, and the desk were completely covered. He motioned them inside and to take a seat in the two seats across from the desk, the only two areas not covered with stacks of papers. He asked them to tell him everything they knew.

Julie knew more than Rollo and explained everything from the beginning to the end. She explained about the mysterious hiking trip but said she wasn't sure if it was legitimate, even though she had never known Max to lie.

The sheriff sat and soaked it all in with authentic concern. The phone rang and the sheriff answered. After a brief conversation he hung up. "That was Deputy Collins," he explained. "He said there was no one at the professor's house, and there were no vehicles there. Is there any other place you think they could be?"

Rollo and Julie tried to think, but it was frustrating, especially for Julie.

Another deputy walked in and stuck out a piece of paper for the sheriff.

Rollo and Julie weren't the only ones frustrated. "Just tell me what it says," the sheriff barked.

The deputy pulled it back. "It's from Professor Nowak's bank, sir. They can't provide numbers or specifics without a court order, but they can tell us that the professor recently almost emptied his savings account."

"Would they say how much?" asked the sheriff.

"Just ballpark. Neighborhood of forty thousand."

The sheriff looked across at the college kids and was already dreading his next question. "You say that Max and the professor were really close?"

"Yes," answered Julie, without even picking up on the insinuation.

Rollo caught it. "Whoa! Whoa, dude. You're barking up the wrong tree. We never said they were close like that."

Julie dropped her head as she too finally understood the implication. Looking back up she said, "That's not even possible. You would have to know Max. He couldn't even think something like that."

"This is his girlfriend," Rollo said, continuing the defense.

"Is that right?" the sheriff asked.

Julie nodded, even though neither she nor Max had actually ever used that word.

"Look, guys," the sheriff said, defending his position, "I promise you my goal is to find them. Period. OK?"

They nodded.

"You guys go on back to campus, and we'll call you if we have more questions or if we find out anything. I appreciate you guys coming down. I really do."

Julie and Rollo got up and left the office.

"What do you think?" asked the deputy.

The sheriff got up and looked out the window. "I honestly don't know. I know those kids believe what they're saying and I hope they're right. But a professor spending a lot of time with a student over summer break, time that they classify themselves as secret, and right before the fall semester the professor withdraws a huge amount of cash and they both disappear. It just doesn't look good; that's all I can say."

"I'll keep digging," the deputy said as he got up to leave the office.

The sheriff nodded without turning around, but continued looking out the window as if the answer would appear there.

An hour later, the sheriff was still glued to his desk. They had checked every public park and hiking area, and no one had seen anyone that matched the description of the professor or Max and no one had seen their vehicles.

The same deputy entered the office again.

"Tell me you got something," the sheriff pleaded.

"I'm not sure," the deputy said. "But I found out the professor owns another property in Michigan. It's right across the line, only about 50 miles from here."

The sheriff looked at his watch. It was already 2:30 p.m. "OK, call Collins."

The deputy called Deputy Collins and put the sheriff's phone on speaker.

"Collins," came the deputy's voice over the speaker.

"Hey, Mike. We just found out that the professor owns a house right across the Michigan border about fifty minutes from here. You feel like a road trip?"

"You bet. Just get me some good directions."

"Yeah, I'm going to have Eugene here get on the computer and lead you right to it."

"Sounds good."

"One more thing, Mike," the sheriff added.

"Yeah?" Deputy Collins asked.

"If you get there and there's anything there at all, let's contact the sheriff up there before we do anything."

"Roger."

The sheriff leaned back in his chair. His ulcer was burning as he realized he hadn't eaten lunch. He told his deputy that he was going to the diner and to call him if he heard anything. He got up and left the building.

An hour later, he was leaving the diner when his cell phone rang.

"Sheriff Furgerson."

The sheriff stopped in his tracks as he listened intensely. His eyes shifted from side to side as the one-sided conversation continued. He held the phone away from his ear for a few seconds and stared at it as if it was the phone itself delivering the message.

"Can you repeat that?" he whispered as he put the phone back to his ear. "Are you on your way back? Good. I want a complete report on my desk within 30 minutes of when you get back."

32

Rollo and Julie sat quietly in the cafeteria. It was an uncommonly bright day outside, which made the cafeteria dark by comparison, and the light filtering through the windows made eerie shadows of everything in the room. Rollo's eyes scanned around and absorbed all the darkness, and he wondered how his once-favorite place on campus could now seem so lifeless and devoid of warmth. It felt almost like a tomb, and it seemed like there wasn't enough air in the room, as Rollo couldn't stop concentrating on his breathing. He tried to focus on Julie, as the more he forced his breathing, the dizzier he became.

He watched as people would come and go with food and drinks, envying their carefree actions and wished that he, too, could focus on simpler things instead of his mind holding him captive as his thoughts played out the many scenarios as to what could have happened to his friend.

When he looked at Julie, he could see in her face that those feelings were magnified. She sat motionless like a Greek statue, a statue carved out of stone to reflect an epic tragedy. Rollo didn't want to leave her alone, but was uncharacteristically at a loss for words. He had asked her several times if she wanted something to eat or drink, but each time she had only shook her head as she sat there staring off into the distance.

Finally, Rollo didn't ask, but got up and went to the serving area and returned with a glass of lemonade. "Here, drink this. It'll make you feel better," he said as he slid it across to Julie.

She began to sip the liquid through the straw, but it seemed unclear if she was even aware she was doing it. Her bloodshot eyes made the blue almost fluorescent as she continued the blank gaze into nothingness.

Several miles away, the sheriff sat at his desk with the same blank stare. He kept going over in his mind what Deputy Collins had told him, but it didn't make sense. He had been in law enforcement for over 20 years and had never encountered anything like this. He wasn't sure exactly how to handle the situation, but he knew the next step. He picked up the phone and dialed.

"This is Sheriff Furgerson. Is this Mr. Maxwell? Or do I call you reverend? . . . OK, Robert it is. I do have some information for you. The details are kind of sketchy, and I'm not sure exactly what's going on, but at least we know where they went. It would be best if I could come by there if that would be alright. Can you give me your address and directions?"

As the sheriff scribbled on an empty envelope, Deputy Collins came into his office carrying a manila folder. When he got off the phone to Reverend Maxwell, he looked up and asked, "Is that it?"

Collins nodded and handed the folder across the desk to the sheriff.

"What do you make of " asked the sheriff.

Collins shook his head. "I don't know what to make of it.'

"Did you touch anything?"

"No," Collins replied. "left it just like I found it."

***

Max's mom sat on the sofa in the little house as the reverend stood by the window with the curtain drawn. It was getting dark outside so he wanted to make sure the sheriff didn't miss their house.

"What did he say again?" asked Max's mom.

Without turning from the window, the reverend answered. "He just said they have information. That's all he said."

The reverend's face was suddenly illuminated as headlights flooded the living room.

"There he is."

He walked over and opened the door to let the sheriff know he was at the right place. He stayed there until the sheriff got out of his car and walked up to the door. He motioned him in and asked him to have a seat in the chair across from the sofa.

The sheriff walked in with the manila folder in his hands.

"Why don't you have a seat, too," the sheriff suggested.

The reverend went back over and sat beside his wife. He sat perfectly erect, his hands cupped over each knee. Only a small imitation-wood coffee table separated them, with only an old family Bible resting on the coffee table.

Max's mom sat with her hands cupped together and pressed into her waist.

The sheriff swallowed hard as he stared down at the folder and tried to think how best to begin. "Do you know what it was they were working on?" he asked.

"No," Max's mom said. "But he was real excited about it."

"He was obsessed with it," the reverend corrected.

The sheriff looked down at the folder again. "It would probably be easiest if I just read this. This is from the professor's house in Lenawee County Michigan." He took out the top page only and began to read.

```
"Deputy Collins arrived on the scene at
3:30 p.m. There he spotted two vehicles
and the license plates confirm that they
belong to Johnny Maxwell and Ronald Nowak.
There were electrical wires running from
the house to what appeared to be a storm
shelter in the back-yard. There was a
hole in the ground that would indicate
a rather large explosion. Debris was
scattered throughout the yard. Pieces
```

```
of concrete, metal, and plastic were
found around the hole.  Also found were
pieces of clothing and flesh.  There were
two wallets located that would indicate
that the two deceased are most likely
Professor Nowak and Johnny Maxwell."
```

The sheriff looked back up again. The reverend still sat in the same position, but now was staring out the window. His hands still rested atop his knees but were now formed into fists that were being squeezed so tight that the blood had rushed away from the fingers and knuckles, leaving them almost white. The mom's hands were still buried into her waist, but her upper body had collapsed across her legs. Her large glasses had slipped off one of her ears and now dangled precariously off the other, her body shaking with violent and uncontrollable spasms.

The sheriff could hardly maintain his composure. He knew this was part of the job, but he wished it wasn't. He had been in law enforcement for a long time, but this was something that never got e i . t va o e i t pr ct d s ve b t o he the bearer o t e c st w a o eo is e y e e h r their entire f w s o th i t eig ed ea i or h s ea Every ime is a ee h t d ee orc d o tl is se m to bruise hi v ry s l, a i s r tha vou d e r g o w y.

H e v r ec sa so r h ire y t th n bu r o or came to i d A d e as v re w e e ca a le o looked down to finish the report.

```
"Death was instantaneous so they didn't
suffer. The blast also ignited the house,
which burned to the ground.  It caused
another explosion from within the base-
ment that destroyed everything. Nothing
was recovered from the house at all."
```

He placed the report back in the investigation folder, stood up, and walked to the door.   He opened the door to let himself out, but paused. Looking back, he added the only words of comfort he could think to say.

"At least they've gone to a better place."

***